James Webb Space Telescope

DEEP SPACE DIARY

PRIMARY SCIENCE
Teacher Resource Book

Creative, cross-curricular primary STEM
learning differentiated for ages 7-11

THE CURVED HOUSE kids

The Deep Space Diary is an arts-based STEM learning programme for primary schools
published by Curved House Kids in partnership with the Science and Technology
Facilities Council (STFC). It is designed to support teachers in delivering engaging
lessons relating to the science and engineering behind the James Webb Space
Telescope.

First published 2020
by Curved House Kids Ltd
60 Farringdon Road
London EC1R 3GA

Written by Olivia Johnson with Kristen Harrison and Lucie Stevens
Illustrated by Hannah Coulson
Designed by Alice Connew and Kristen Harrison
Typeset by Constanin Nimigean

A CIP record for this book is available from the British Library.
ISBN: 978-1-913269-15-9

Acknowledgements
The Discovery Diaries would not exist without the European Space Agency astronaut Tim
Peake, author Lucy Hawking and the UK Space Agency. Every new book we create in this
series is built on the legacy of the Principia Space Diary, our first collaboration with these
amazing people and organisations.

Thank you to the Science and Technology Facilities Council (STCF) without whom
the Deep Space Diary would not be possible, and to all the STEM experts who have
contributed to this programme. A special thanks to the incredible team of teachers who
contributed to the programme's teaching resources and to Professor Peter McOwan
at Queen Mary University of London who has provided academic input on all of the
Discovery Diaries.

www.discoverydiaries.org

Printed in the United Kingdom on FSC approved paper.

Developed with support, and in collaboration, with:

Contents

Colour-coded chapters for easy reference

Chapter One: Astronomer's Bootcamp!

Chapter Two: Telescope Training

Chapter Three: Designing for Discovery

Chapter Four: Journey to Deep Space

Chapter Five: Groundbreaking Discoveries

Chapter Six: Space News

Visit www.discoverydiaries.org to download extra content for use in the classroom

Introduction

About the programme

The Deep Space Diary is a free primary STEM programme that combines STEM learning with a breadth of other subjects. By using visual learning, creativity and personalisation, it empowers non-specialist teachers and all students, regardless of interests or abilities. The third book in the Discovery Diaries series, it contains 25 activities themed around the James Webb Space Telescope. The programme is fully supported by teaching notes, lesson plans, suggested teaching schedules, customised curriculum guides, ideas for differentiation, plus digital and web resources, to make teaching flexible and time effective.

Designed for Key Stage 2/P5-7/Y4-6, the Deep Space Diary has been created with a diverse range of real STEM experts, including lead author Dr Olivia Johnson, with the support of the Science and Technology Facilities Council and ESA astronaut Tim Peake. Using the premise of building the world's most powerful telescope and observing our Universe, each diary activity combines a STEM topic with another subject – like English, Art/Design, or History – while building science capital. This cross-curricular approach makes STEM accessible for students who may not be confident in this area, as well as providing teachers with the flexibility to incorporate materials into its activities.

How to use this book

Everything you need to uncover the secrets of the Universe is included in this book. Divided into six chapters, the Deep Space Diary programme will take your students on an adventure through space with the James Webb Space Telescope. Students will study the history of astronomy, explore our Solar System, learn about light, colour and infrared, and even engineer their own telescopes. Activities are designed to be flexible and self-contained, so you can either do them sequentially or select the ones that fit into your existing learning plan.

In each chapter of this book, you'll find the Deep Space Diary activities – ready to photocopy – accompanied by teaching notes that provide background information, ideas on how to run the lesson, questions for the class, extension activities and teaching tips. A list of required resources will ensure you have everything your need, and useful links will guide you to other support materials.

We know how busy educators are, so we've developed a number of resources to streamline your preparation time. In our Teacher Toolkit on page 7, you'll find suggested schedules for running the programme over one week, one half-term or one term. You'll also find a blank lesson plan template, as well as reflection templates for students to reinforce learning.

"The pupils loved it. The interactive element made them engaged from the start! Time effective, excellent lower ability differentiation [and] flexible enough that it allowed the children to progress through it at their own speed."

Amy Broadman, Primary Teacher

60+ hours of STEAM activities, fully supported by teaching notes

Differentiation to both support and challenge students

Extension activities included in every set of teaching notes

Motivate and Incentivise Students

Deep Space Diaries are personalisable workbooks that are hugely popular with students because they encourage ownership, promote sustained engagement and give students (and educators) a lasting record of work. Included in the Deep Space Diary programme are Mission Badges for you to reward students as they complete each chapter. These can be downloaded from the web portal (see below). Printed copies of the Deep Space Diary have their Mission Badges included in the book as stickers. You can also download Completion Certificates, to present to your students once they've finished their diaries.

Tailored Curriculum Guides

For our educators in the UK, we've prepared customised guides for England, Northern Ireland, Scotland and Wales, linking each activity to your region's curriculum. The guides also include ideas for differentiation, to support and challenge every learner. Download the guides from discoverydiaries.org, where you'll also find a wealth of other support resources.

The Discovery Diaries Web Portal

Everything you need to run and enrich your Deep Space Diary programme is available on our website: discoverydiaries.org. Visit the site, create your free account and then log in to access curriculum guides, PowerPoint slides, image bundles, videos and useful links. You'll find all programme resources by clicking 'Resources' in the toolbar and then selecting the Deep Space Diary. You can then navigate the programme chapter-by-chapter, or use the filter in 'Pick-and Mix' to search by programme, subject area, learning methodology or key stage. If an activity includes additional digital content via a lightning bolt 'Zap code', you can access this content on the web portal by visiting that activity's page. For more information on Zap codes, see page 12.

The web portal also includes a 'Meet the Experts' gallery featuring diverse STEM professionals to inspire young learners. You'll also find articles sharing teaching ideas and information about space on our Community page. All the resources on our website are free for you to download and share. Simply log in to start your mission!

Our programmes are proven to work

The Discovery Diary model combines visual, multi-modal and cross-curricular learning methodologies to ensure that every student finds a 'way in' to complex STEM topics. Students are encouraged to imagine, question, research, visualise, analyse, problem solve and to 'think like a scientist'. This unique, holistic approach enables every child to fully connect and participate. Personalisation of the diaries, along with Mission Badges, reward hard work to further encourage deep and sustained engagement in STEM.

The Discovery Diary model was developed with the support of the UK Space Agency, through the creation of the Principia Space Diary featuring ESA astronaut Tim Peake. In their evaluation of the education outreach for Tim Peake's mission, UKSA highlighted the Space Diary as one of the top three standout education programmes.

Original videos including one featuring Tim Peake

Digital content to enhance learning

Regular newsletters for ongoing support

TEACHER TOOLKIT

Our Teacher Toolkit contains a suite of resources to help you plan, run and evaluate your Deep Space Diary programme. Take the guesswork out of planning and follow our suggested schedules – running the programme over a week, half-term or term – refer to our Curriculum Guides to learn how each activity aligns to the curriculum in your region, use our blank lesson plan template to prepare for each class, and evaluate student understanding with our range of reflection templates. You'll find suggested schedules and blank templates in this book. Log onto **discoverydiaries.org** to access our other Toolkit resources, including Mission Badges and completion certificates to acknowledge student progress throughout the programme.

What's inside this section?

Curriculum Overview

Scheduling Plans

Zappar App Instructions

Lesson Plan Template

Student Reflection Sheets

Word Search Template

Student Article Planner

Meet the Experts

Quick Guide to Curriculum Links

Deep Space Diary for Key Stage 2, P5-7, Y4-6
England, Wales, Scotland and Northern Ireland

Lesson no.	Activity Name	Duration	Primary Science/ Working Scientifically	Maths/ Numeracy	English/ Literacy	Computing	D&T	Geography	History	Art & Design	Spiritual, Moral, Social and Cultural
Activity 1.1	To Space and Beyond	45 mins	✓							✓	✓
Activity 1.2	The Sky at Night	60 mins	✓	✓				✓	✓		
Activity 1.3	Ancient Astronomy	60 mins	✓		✓				✓		✓
Activity 1.4	The Starry Messengers	60 mins	✓						✓	✓	
Activity 1.5	Deep Space Quiz	15 mins	✓		✓						
Activity 2.1	Lights, Mirror, Action	60 mins	✓				✓				
Activity 2.2	Make-Your-Own Colour Wheel	45 mins	✓	✓			✓				
Activity 2.3	Recipe for a Rainbow	30-60 mins	✓	✓			✓			✓	
Activity 2.4	Infrared Selfie	60-90 mins	✓							✓	✓
Activity 3.1	Blueprint for Space	60 mins	✓	✓							
Activity 3.2	Mega Mirror Engineer	30-60 mins	✓	✓			✓				
Activity 3.3	Keep it Cool	60-120 mins	✓	✓							✓
Activity 3.4	Pack Your Payload	60-120 mins	✓				✓				
Activity 4.1	Parking Skills	30 mins	✓			✓					
Activity 4.2	Deep Space Decoder	30-45 mins	✓		✓	✓					✓
Activity 4.3	Calibrate for Discovery	45 mins	✓	✓							
Activity 5.1	First Findings	30-60 mins	✓			✓				✓	
Activity 5.2	Data Detective	45 mins	✓								✓
Activity 5.3	Visualising the Universe	30-60 mins	✓		✓					✓	✓
Activity 6.1	Deep Space Daily	120-180 mins	✓		✓					✓	✓
Activity 6.2	Visual Dictionary of Deep Space	Ongoing	✓		✓					✓	✓
Throughout	Word searches	15 mins	✓		✓						✓

Teacher Timeline: Space-Themed Week

Run an immersive, cross-curricular space-themed week

	MONDAY Astronomer's Bootcamp	TUESDAY Deep Space Discovery	WEDNESDAY Journey to Deep Space	THURSDAY Groundbreaking Discoveries	FRIDAY Deep Space Reporter
Morning	Introduction (15 mins) **Activity 1.1** To Space and Beyond (45 mins) **Activity 1.2** The Sky at Night (60 mins)	**Activity 2.3** Recipe for a Rainbow (30-60 mins) **Activity 2.4** Infrared Selfie (60-90 mins) Chapter 2 Word Search	**Activity 3.4** Pack Your Payload (60-120 mins) Chapter 3 Word Search	**Activity 5.3** Visualising the Universe (60 mins) Chapter 5 Word Search	**Activity 6.1** Deep Space Daily Parts 2 & 3 (90 mins)
Break					
Mid-Morning	**Activity 1.3** Ancient Astronomy (60 mins) **Activity 1.4** The Starry Messengers (60 mins) Reflection Q&A	**Activity 3.1** Blueprint for Space (60 mins) **Activity 3.2** Mega Mirror Engineer (30-60 mins)	**Activity 4.1** Parking Skills (30 mins) **Activity 4.2** Deep Space Decoder (30-45 mins) **Activity 4.3** Calibrate for Discovery (45 mins)	**Deep Space Review** Allow students to collate/expand research across week, providing access to books/internet. **Activity 6.2** Visual Dictionary of Deep Space	**Mission Debrief** Share and feedback, Q&A. Students could use this time to make a presentation on their week and present to parents in the afternoon.
Lunch					
Afternoon	**Activity 1.5** Deep Space Quiz (15 mins) **Activity 2.1** Lights, Mirror, Action (60 mins) **Activity 2.2** Make-Your-Own Colour Wheel (<5 mins)	**Activity 3.3** Keep it Cool (60-120 mins)	**Chapter 4 Word Search** **Activity 5.1** First Findings (30-60 mins) **Activity 5.2** Data Detective (45 mins)	**Activity 6.1** Deep Space Daily Parts 1 & 2 (90 mins)	Sharing assembly, parents invited. Students present their work and findings.
Home Learning (Optional)	**Stargazing/Moongazing:** Get out and see the stars. Can you find any constellations, satellites or the ISS?	Make-Your-Own Telescope	Art inspired by space	Creative writing inspired by space	

Teacher Timeline:
One Half Term

Weekly 90-120 minute science lessons over an entire term

	Activity Suggested	Curriculum Links	Optional Home Learning
Week 1	Introduce Deep Space Diary (15 mins) **Activity 1.1** To Space and Beyond (45 mins) **Activity 1.2** The Sky at Night (60 mins)	English; Maths; Working Scientifically	Art inspired by space
Week 2	**Activity 1.3** Ancient Astronomy (60 mins) **Activity 1.4** The Starry Messengers (60 mins) **Activity 1.5** Deep Space Quiz (15 mins)	English; Maths; Science; Working Scientifically; DT; SMSC/TSPC	Make-Your-Own model of the Solar System
Week 3	**Activity 2.1** Lights, Mirror, Action (60 mins) **Activity 2.2** Make-Your-Own Colour Wheel (45 mins)	English; Maths; Science; Working Scientifically; Art; SMSC/TSPC	Make-Your-Own telescope Magic tricks with light
Week 4	**Activity 2.3** Recipe for a Rainbow (30-60 mins) **Activity 2.4** Infrared Selfie (60-90 mins) Chapter 2 Word Search	English; Maths; Science; Working Scientifically; Art; SMSC/TSPC	Research IR imaging and its uses
Week 5	**Activity 3.1** Blueprint for Space (60 mins) **Activity 3.2** Mega Mirror Engineer (30-60 mins)	English; Maths; Science; Working Scientifically	Create a piece of writing demonstrating research on the James Webb Space Telescope
Week 6	**Activity 3.3** Keep it Cool (60-120 mins) Chapter 3 Word Search	English; Maths; Science; Working Scientifically; SMSC/TSPC	Space poems
Week 7	**Activity 4.1** Parking Skills (30 mins) **Activity 4.2** Deep Space Decoder (30-45 mins) **Activity 4.3** Calibrate for Discovery (45 mins) Chapter 4 Word Search	English; Maths; Science; Working Scientifically; Geography; Computing; History	Create your own space code
Week 8	**Activity 5.1** First Findings (30-60 mins) **Activity 5.2** Data Detective (45 mins) **Activity 5.3** Visualising the Universe (60 mins)	English; Maths; Science; Working Scientifically; Art; Computing; History	Timeline of telescopes
Week 9	Chapter 5 Word Search **Activity 6.1** Deep Space Daily (90-120 mins) Mission Debrief	English; Science; Working Scientifically; Computing	Independent model-making and research

Teacher Timeline:
One Full Term

Weekly 60-90 minute science lessons over an entire term

	Activity Suggested	Curriculum Links	Optional Home Learning
Week 1	Introduce Deep Space Diary (15 mins) **Activity 1.1** To Space and Beyond (45 mins)	English; Maths; Working Scientifically	
Week 2	**Activity 1.2** The Sky at Night (60 mins) **Activity 1.3** Ancient Astronomy (60 mins)	English; Maths; Science; Working Scientifically; Art; SMSC/TSPC	Make-your-own model of the Solar System
Week 3	Finish Activity 1.3 Ancient Astronomy **Activity 1.4** The Starry Messengers (60 mins)	English; Maths; Science; Working Scientifically; Art; SMSC/TSPC	Stargazing: Go outside and observe the night sky/moon
Week 4	**Activity 1.5** Deep Space Quiz (15 mins) **Activity 2.1** Lights, Mirror, Action (60 mins)	English; Maths; Science; Working Scientifically	Make-your-own telescope Magic tricks with light
Week 5	**Activity 2.2** Make-Your-Own Colour Wheel (45 mins) **Activity 2.3** Recipe for a Rainbow (30-60 mins)	English; Maths; Science; Working Scientifically; Art; SMSC/TSPC	Create a piece of writing demonstrating research on the James Webb Space Telescope
Week 6	**Activity 2.4** Infrared Selfie (60-90 mins) Chapter 2 Word Search	English; Maths; Science; Working Scientifically; Geography; Computing; History	Art inspired by space
Week 7	**Activity 3.1** Blueprint for Space (60 mins) **Activity 3.2** Mega Mirror Engineer (30-60 mins)	English; Maths; Science; Working Scientifically	Independent model-making and research
Week 8	**Activity 3.3** Keep it Cool (60-120 mins)	English; Maths; Science; Geography	Research IR imaging and its uses
Week 9	Chapter 3 Word Search **Activity 4.1** Parking Skills (30 mins)	English; Maths; Science; Working Scientifically; Geography; Computing; History	Timeline of telescopes
Week 10	**Activity 4.2** Deep Space Decoder (30-45 mins) **Activity 4.3** Calibrate for Discovery (45 mins) Chapter 4 Word Search	English; Maths; Science; Working Scientifically; Art; Computing; History	Space poems
Week 11	**Activity 5.1** First Findings (30-60 mins) **Activity 5.2** Data Detective (45 mins)	English; Maths; Science; Working Scientifically; Computing; History	Create your own space code
Week 12	**Activity 5.3** Visualising the Universe (60 mins)	English; Working Scientifically; Computing; History	Independent model-making and research
Week 13	Chapter 5 Word Search **Activity 6.1** Deep Space Daily: Research & Writing (90-120 mins)	English; Science; Working Scientifically; Computing	Presentations inspired by the Deep Space Diary: this could include diary entries, letters to astronauts, creative writing, models, quizzes or research into subjects raised through the programme. Present the following week, perhaps as part of an assembly to parents.
Week 14	**Activity 6.1:** Deep Space Daily: Editing & Publishing (90-120 mins) Mission Debrief	English; Science; Working Scientifically; Computing	

HOW TO USE ZAP CODES

Many of our activities include a **Zap code** allowing your students to access extra content through a smart phone, tablet or other device. All you need to do is download the free Zappar App. If you don't have access to tablets or devices in the classroom, all the zap code content is available to download for offline use on our website. Simply navigate to the activity's page to find Image Bundles, PowerPoints and more. Try it now and take a selfie with Tim Peake!

1. Ready
Download the Zappar App to your mobile or tablet

2. Aim
Open Zappar and hold your device in front of this unique zap code

4. Share your pics with Tim!
Post your image on Twitter or Instagram and share with Tim by using @astro_timpeake. Don't forget to use **#discoverydiaries** so we can share your pics!

3. Zap!
Content will appear on your phone that relates to the activity (or in this case, Tim will appear!)

Lesson Planner

Date:

Learning Objective:
Curriculum Links:
Absentees:

Hook / Starter:

Main Activities:

Reflection:

Differentiation:

Follow up required:

Next steps:

REFLECTION

Create a mind-map of what you've learnt. Can you represent something you have learnt as a picture or a cartoon?

RECAP!

Write a reflection on what you've learnt:

RECAP!

Create a list to summarise what you've learnt:

1. _____

2. _____

3. _____

4. _____

5. _____

6. _____

7. _____

8. _____

9. _____

10. _____

RECAP!

Create your own quiz from facts you've learnt, and test
your friends!

TRUE FALSE

1. _ ☐ ☐

2. _ ☐ ☐

3. _ ☐ ☐

4. _ ☐ ☐

5. _ ☐ ☐

6. _ ☐ ☐

7. _ ☐ ☐

James Webb Space Telescope
**DEEP SPACE
DIARY**

'S WORD SEARCH

Choose eight SPACE themed words and write them up, down, forwards, backwards or diagonally into this word search. Fill up the empty squares with random letters and challenge your friends!

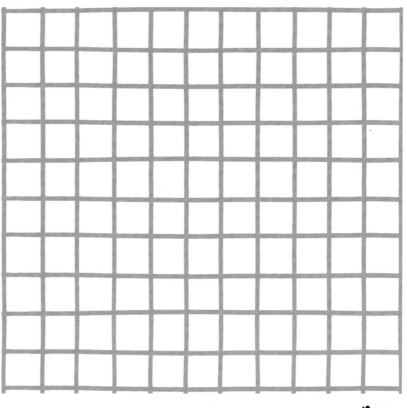

Write your words here!

'S WORD SEARCH

Choose eight SPACE themed words and write them up, down, forwards, backwards or diagonally into this word search. Fill up the empty squares with random letters and challenge your friends!

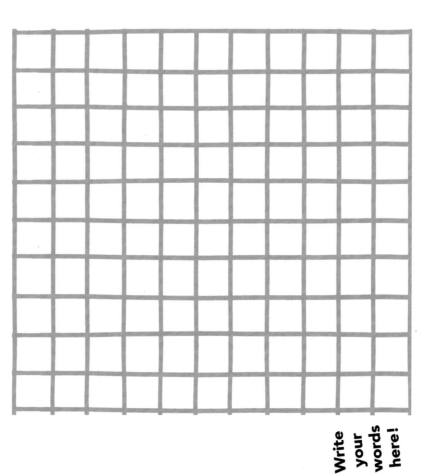

Write your words here!

Article Planner

Headline:

Opening Statement

Who?

What?

When?

Where?

Why?

Paragraph 1:

Paragraph 2:

Paragraph 3:

Closing Statement:

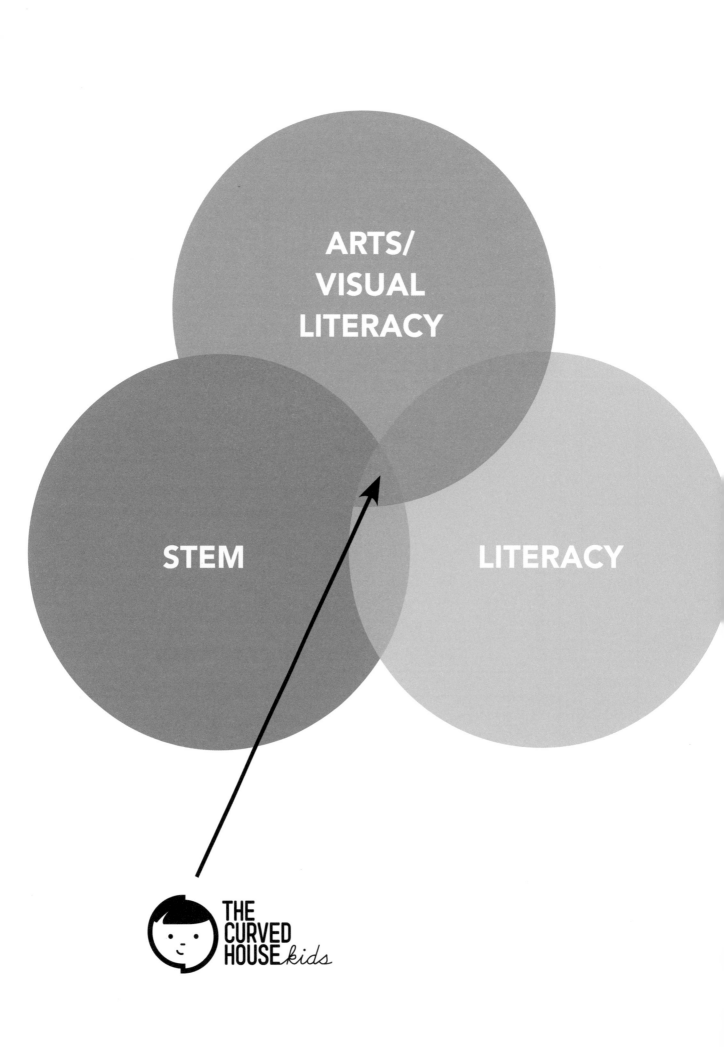

Meet the Experts

The Deep Space Diary profiles real STEM experts with diverse careers and backgrounds, to showcase the range of career paths available in the space sector. Our interviews with both men and women – working in roles across the sciences and engineering – will inspire your students. In particular, they're a great way to empower girls and students who are under-represented in the sector.

Olivia Johnson – Astronomer (p22)
As Public Engagement Manager at the Royal Observatory Edinburgh, Olivia shares her passion for astronomy with children and adults, so that they can learn about our wondrous Universe.

Tim Peake – ESA Astronaut (p24)
Tim is a British astronaut who spent six months on the International Space Station in 2015-16. During his time in space, Tim conducted over 250 scientific experiments.

Gillian Wright – Director of UK Astronomy Technology Centre (p36)
Gillian has led the large team of scientists across the UK and Europe who designed, built and installed Webb's Mid-Infrared Instrument (MIRI).

Martyn Wells – Optical Engineer (p57)
Using his knowledge of how light moves and bends, Martyn was involved in designing Webb's lenses and mirrors.

Piyal Samara-Ratna – Mechanical Engineer (p71)
Piyal was a member of the engineering team for Webb's MIRI – one of four instruments on the telescope that capture infrared light from outer space.

Vincent Geers – Software Engineer (p95)
As well as being a software engineer, Vincent is also an astronomer. Like Piyal, he worked on Webb's MIRI.

Pamela Klaassen – Instrument Scientist (p99)
Pamela worked on Webb's special instruments which measure and analyse the spectrum, so we can study the Universe.

Alastair Bruce – Astronomer (p108)
Alastair splits his work life between studying distant galaxies and helping people learn more about Webb, sharing exciting news about discoveries firsthand.

Beth Biller – Reader (p112)
Beth works at the Institute of Astronomy of the University of Edinburgh, researching planets in other solar systems.

Naomi Rowe-Gurney – PhD Student (p116)
Using data collected by telescopes, Naomi studies what the atmospheres of ice giant planets Uranus and Neptune are made of and how they've changed over time.

Begin your exploration of deep space by reading and discussing the introduction by Dr Olivia Johnson...

WELCOME, SPACE EXPLORER!

Welcome to Team Webb! You are about to embark on one of the most difficult space missions of all time. You will oversee the design, engineering, construction and launch of the most powerful space telescope that has ever existed. And that's just the beginning...

Your groundbreaking telescope will be able to spot the first galaxies ever formed, peer inside dusty cocoons where new stars are born and even study the air around alien planets. Once you have safely launched it, you will use your telescope to collect data and report back on what you discover.

Go forth, brave explorer. We are waiting to see the Universe through your eyes!

GOOD LUCK!
Olivia Johnson
and the Space Crew

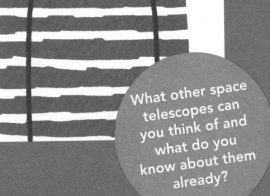

What other space telescopes can you think of and what do you know about them already?

What skills can you bring to a challenging space mission like this, and what do you want to learn?

CHAPTER 1: ASTRONOMER'S BOOTCAMP!

For centuries, humans have been using the night sky to navigate and measure time. Set your students up for a successful mission to deep space by exploring how we've looked at the sky in the past, what we've discovered and what we are yet to learn.

What do you imagine a "dusty cocoon" looks like – can you draw it?

What's inside this chapter?

1.1 – To Space and Beyond
Watch a special video message from ESA astronaut Tim Peake, then imagine a deep space discovery.
> Science + Art

1.2 – The Sky at Night
Plot the coordinates to identify a star formation visible with the naked eye.
> Science + Maths

1.3 – Ancient Astronomy
Analyse an ancient diagram of the Solar System to identify what humans have learnt over time.
> Science + History

1.4 – The Starry Messengers
Learn about the history of astronomy and the development of the telescope.
> Science + History

1.5 – The Deep Space Quiz
Write a 'true or false' quiz about the history of space observation.
> Science + Literacy

TO SPACE AND BEYOND...

Do you ever wonder what's out there in the Universe?

Zap to watch a video message from Tim Peake

Hi space explorer, ESA astronaut Tim Peake here!

When I was on the International Space Station, I'd look out of the window and imagine what we might find if we could travel into deep space. If you had the power to see more of the Universe than anyone has before, what would you want to discover?

Draw or write what you want to discover

Activity 1.1: To Space and Beyond

Background to this Activity

The development of technology has enabled us to learn more about our Solar System and explore the Universe we live in. For example, in 2005 the Hubble Space Telescope discovered two new moons in our Solar System, orbiting Pluto. Since 1990, Hubble has helped scientists study space. After its last service by astronauts in 2015, NASA decided it would not be repaired again. Now, a new era of space exploration is underway, led by the largest telescope humans have built to date – the James Webb Space Telescope.

Known as Webb, the James Webb Space Telescope has the potential to significantly advance our understanding of the Universe. Webb's huge primary mirror is more than twice the size of Hubble's, allowing it to collect vast amounts of light and detect light from fainter objects in space. This, along with its specialist instruments that are designed to detect infrared wavelengths, allows it to observe stars and planets forming and to see the light emitted by galaxies in the early Universe.

Webb has four key study goals:

- First Light: When did the first stars start to shine?

- Galaxy Building: How do galaxies like the Milky Way form?

- The Birth of Stars and Planets: What is happening within the clouds of gas and dust which form stars, and how do the 'leftovers' of this process evolve to become planets?

- Exoplanets and the Origins of Life: Scientists suspect that galaxies are teeming with planets. They would like to discover if any of those planets are similar to Earth.

Running the Activity

This activity is designed to promote imaginative and lateral thinking.

Begin by drawing on students' existing knowledge to create a mind-map of what they already know about Earth and space. This could be done as a class or in small groups. Before starting the main activity, access Tim Peake's message using a smartphone, device or through the web portal – see Useful Links.

Resources Required

- Tablet or device to access Zap code (optional — see Useful Links)

- Art supplies

Useful Links

Visit **discoverydiaries.org/activities/ to-space-and-beyond** to download Zappar app content to use offline (PowerPoints, videos and image bundles etc.) and to access links to other info, which may be useful in planning and running this lesson.

Using the concept of space as an endless frontier, ask students to generate ideas and questions about what humans might discover if they had the power to see more of the Universe than ever before, noting these on a whiteboard or whiteboard paper. If in small groups, students can take turns asking each other what they would like to discover most about our Universe. After their discussion, students should have an idea of a question or concept they would most like to explore. They can capture this through art, diagramming, writing or images on their activity sheet – this will become their mission goal.

Questions for the Class

- Where is Earth positioned in our Solar System?

- Which other celestial bodies are in our Solar System?

- Are there any other celestial bodies you know about? What are they?

- What is a star?

- Can stars have planets around them?

- What else might be in outer space that we don't know about yet?

- What can stop us from seeing further into space?

- Other than planets and stars, what else can be found in space?

Additional Challenges / Extension Activities

Research our Galaxy – the Milky Way – and identify our Solar System's position in it. Other than our Solar System, what else might we find in the Milky Way?

Planning an enquiry: Now that students have their mission goal, can they break down the steps, or explain how they would go about finding out the answer to their question? Question them about evidence they may need to collect in order to support their idea or possible answer.

Non-chronological Report/ Explanation text: Using their research into our Galaxy, can students communicate their findings scientifically?

Ideas for Differentiation

Support:

- Support students by working in small groups. Provide students with vocabulary and a suitable glossary for celestial bodies, such as planet, sun, moon, star, exoplanet, asteroid, comet, atmosphere, black hole, galaxy, dark matter. Understanding of these terms could be further supported by providing definitions and images of each word. See the Deep Space Glossary for terms and definitions – see Useful Links.

**Got notes?
Write them
here!**

_____

_____

_____

_____

_____

_____

_____

_____

Challenge:

- Linked to the planning an enquiry extension, ask students to write a Mission Request letter to Tim Peake, explaining what they want to discover, why they want to discover it and what they will need to complete their mission.

Teacher Tip!

If you don't have internet access in your classroom, download Tim Peake's video message from discoverydiaries. org beforehand. You'll find the video on the activity page.

THE SKY AT NIGHT

Long before there were telescopes, humans observed stars and planets with the naked eye. What can you see when you look up at the night sky? Plot the coordinates below to reveal a star formation you may recognise!

	Star Name	Coordinates	
◆	Dubhe	x -3,	y -3
✕	Merak	x -5,	y -1
☐	Phecda	x -3,	y 1
●	Megrez	x -1,	y 0
■	Alioth	x 1,	y 1
○	Mizar	x 3,	y 2
▲	Alkaid	x 4,	y 4

Use these symbols to mark each star

Do you recognise this star pattern?

Zap for the answer

Activity 1.2: The Sky at Night

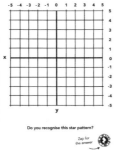

Background to this Activity

Since ancient times, humans have used the celestial bodies (stars and planets) to monitor the passing of time, to navigate and for cultural and religious ceremonies. As early as the mid-seventeenth century BCE, humans were recording the movements of planets. This means they had recognised the difference between stars, which retain their configuration in the sky over time, and planets which change position in relation to these stars.

The 'Plough' is an asterism (a small pattern of stars) which is always visible in the Northern Hemisphere, regardless of the season. It consists of seven bright stars, four which form the 'body' or moldboard of the plough and three which create the 'handle'.

When we look at the Plough from Earth, its position in relation to where we are viewing it from will change according to the season and the time of night. Because the Earth spins on an axis, the Plough completes a rotation around the North Star every 24 hours.

Running the Activity

Introduce the concept that humans have used stars for navigation and to monitor the passing of time for centuries. NB: If students are unaware of vocabulary, such as celestial bodies and constellations, go through this with the class at beginning of activity and refer to the glossary – see Useful Links. Ask students to think about why this might be. Using a globe, demonstrate how the Earth spins on an axis, creating day and night. The angle of Earth's axis can also help students understand why we see different stars in different hemispheres.

To explain why constellations (groups of stars which form recognisable patterns) appear to rotate during the night, ask students to stand below something that is fixed to the ceiling, such as a rectangular fluorescent light fitting. Tell the students to look up and slowly turn on the spot. As they move, the orientation of the light fitting will change from the child's point of view. The activity works even

Resources Required

- Tablet or device to access Zap code (optional — see Useful Links)
- World globe (optional)

Useful Links

Visit **discoverydiaries.org/ activities/the-sky-at-night** to download Zappar app content to use offline (PowerPoints, videos and image bundles etc.) and to access links to other info, which may be useful in planning and running this lesson.

better if students can stand beneath a picture attached to the ceiling, which will appear upside-down to each student as they spin. As a group, discuss why the movement of constellations created by Earth's rotation would have been useful for humans before we had technology to measure time and identify our location on Earth.

Explain to the class that they will be plotting an asterism made of seven stars on the axis and that each star has a name. Students should work through the coordinates, plotting each star by using its symbol. Students can then draw a line from star to star to reveal the Plough's shape. Using the Zap code, they can then identify the name of the asterism and confirm that their plotting is correct.

Solution to the Activity

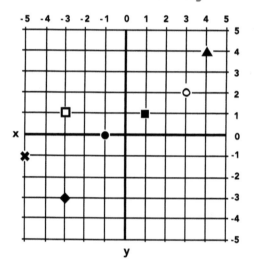

Questions for the Class

- What are some of the differences between stars and planets?

- Why do people in different hemispheres (*halves of the Earth – remember hemi = half, sphere is a shape. Two hemispheres make a sphere – the shape of the Earth*) see different constellations?

- Why do constellations appear to move during the night?

- Besides the movement of constellations, what are some other ways we can monitor the time of day, month or year, without using modern technology?

Additional Challenges / Extension Activities

The Plough is the name of this asterism in the UK, but other cultures have their own names for it. Ask students to research the various names of the Plough – in both contemporary and past cultures – identifying where each name is used both geographically and historically.

The Plough is an asterism – a small collection of stars which is part of a constellation. Ask students to research which constellation the Plough is in (Ursa Major), and ask them to learn about its name and the mythology/ story behind it.

Got notes? Write them here!

Identify other constellations which appear in the Northern Hemisphere and plot them on black cardboard using star stickers, to create a constellation gallery in the classroom.

Ideas for Differentiation

Support:

- Support younger students by working through the coordinates as a group. If you have an outdoor playground available, draw the graph in chalk and guide students in physically plotting coordinates by assigning seven students the role of 'star' and the rest of the class as 'astronomers'. Students can then work together to plot the asterism on their worksheets.

Challenge:

- Recreate the graph on an A3 piece of paper, extending both axes five times to 25. Ask students to plot the Plough, labelling each star with its name. Next, ask students to find the position of Polaris – the North Star – which is located by drawing an imaginary line from Merak to Dubhe, then extending it for five times the distance between these two stars. Students can then identify the coordinates of Polaris.

Teacher Tip!

Using chalk, drawn a huge grid in the playground, then allocate the role of 'star' to seven students. The remaining students can be 'astronomers', guiding the stars into place.

ANCIENT ASTRONOMY

Zap to explore our Solar System

Throughout history, humans have used the night sky as a map, a clock and a calendar. But before telescopes were invented we didn't always understand our Solar System, especially where Earth was in relation to other planets. Can you see Earth in the diagram below?

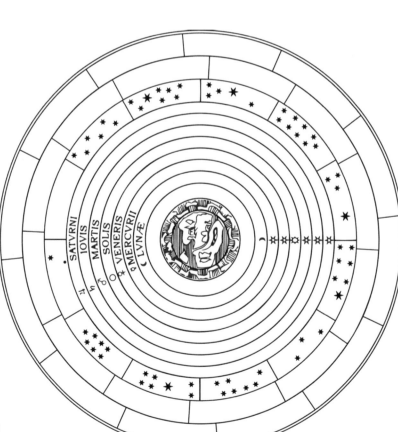

Ancient Diagram of our Solar System

Draw your own diagram of the Solar System based on our knowledge of it today. How does this compare to the ancient diagram on the left? What have we learnt?

Modern Diagram of our Solar System

Activity 1.3: Ancient Astronomy

Ancient Diagram of our Solar System   Modern Diagram of our Solar System

Background to this Activity

Our Solar System is made up of eight planets, two dwarf planets (Ceres and Pluto), at least 187 moons, and millions of comets, asteroids and meteors. Although astronomers in ancient times – like Aristarchus of Samos who lived in Greece in the third century BCE – theorised that the planets orbited the Sun, many people believed that the Earth was the centre of the Solar System until the 1500s. This theory was promoted by Aristotle's *On the Heavens*, written in 350BCE. The sketch included in this activity is based on Aristotelean cosmology.

In 1543, Copernicus' book *On the Revolutions of the Heavenly Bodies* was published. It proposed a heliocentric model of our Solar System, which differed from the geocentric model proposed by Ptolemy in the second century CE, in which all celestial bodies orbited the Earth. In 1609, Galileo invented a spy glass or telescope that allowed him to observe the mountains on the Moon, the phases of Venus, Saturn's rings and Jupiter's four brightest moons. The scientific observations made by Galileo supported the theory of a heliocentric Solar System.

Key vocabulary

Helio – Sun
Geo – Earth
Centric – at the centre
Model – a three-dimensional representation of a proposed structure, often at a smaller scale

Running the Activity

This activity supports the development of visual analysis – an important skill for scientists.

Begin by asking students to examine the Aristotelean diagram of the Solar System on the left-hand page of the worksheet. Ask them to volunteer observations about the diagram. What do they notice that differs from their existing knowledge of the Solar System? What's missing? What's in the wrong position? What do they think the words mean?

Ask students when they think this diagram might have been drawn.

Resources Required

- Tablet or device to access Zap code (optional — see Useful Links)
- Rulers
- Compasses

Useful Links

Visit **discoverydiaries.org/ activities/ancient-astronomy** to download Zappar app content to use offline (PowerPoints, videos and image bundles etc.) and to access links to other info, which may be useful in planning and running this lesson.

Invite discussion about how our understanding of the Solar System may have developed over time.

Revisit the structure of our Solar System, then ask students to draw it on the worksheet, encouraging different levels of accuracy concerning the shape of orbital paths and distances of the planets from the Sun, based on student ability. More capable students can be introduced to Astronomical Units, which is covered in Mars Diary Activity 2.1: Going the Distance.

Solutions to the Activity

See Useful Links.

Questions for the Class

- Why couldn't ancient astronomers see all of the planets in our Solar System?

- Do planets orbit the Sun at the same speed? How can we tell how quickly they are orbiting?

- Why causes day and night?

- What causes our daytime length to change over the course of a year?

Additional Challenges / Extension Activities

Mnemonics are a great way to help students remember the order of the planets e.g. My very educated mother just served us noodles; Ask students to write their own mnemonic to help them remember.

As a class, create a large-scale diagram of the Solar System, including other objects in space like asteroid belts, the ISS, moons, manmade satellites, comets, etc.

Looking at the words on the ancient diagram on the worksheet, ask students to research what the different words mean.

Important astronomical discoveries were made across the world in ancient times. Islamic astronomers like Al-Battani, al-Sufi, al-Biruni, and Ibn Yunus recorded the position of the Sun, Moon and stars; the Ancient Mayans built structures like staircases and wells to align with astronomical events and made many detailed records of celestial movements; during the Shang Dynasty, Chinese astronomers produced a calendar of the moon cycle; in the Southern Hemisphere, indigenous Australians had developed astronomical methodologies over 65,000 years ago. Ask students to research an ancient astronomer or culture of their choice.

Ideas for Differentiation

Support:

- Support younger students by using a primer activity like Space Diary Activity 3.4: The Solar System to revise the planets in our Solar System. Work in small groups or pairs to identify the order of the planets. Provide students with

Got notes? Write them here!

_____
_____
_____
_____
_____
_____
_____

cardboard circles of varying size to trace, to position the planets around the Sun.

Challenge:

- Introduce higher ability students to Astronomical Units – the unit of measurement used to measure the distance of planets from the Sun. 1 AU is equal to the distance from our Sun to the Earth. This can be done with a primer activity like Mars Diary Activity 2.1: Going the Distance.

- Challenge students to accurately represent the distance of each planet from the Sun, using a compass to draw each orbital path.

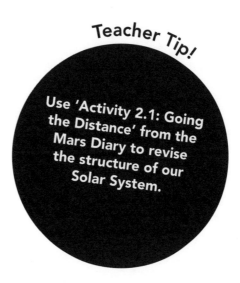

Teacher Tip!

Use 'Activity 2.1: Going the Distance' from the Mars Diary to revise the structure of our Solar System.

_____

_____

_____

_____

_____

_____

_____

_____

THE STARRY MESSENGERS

Throughout the history of astronomy, each new technology has enabled us to discover more and more about the Universe. Travel back in time and draw what each telescope has shown us.

James Webb Space Telescope

Zap to discover more about these awesome telescopes

Hubble Space Telescope

Hi space explorer, I'm Gillian Wright and I lead a team working on the James Webb Space Telescope. Webb has the potential to see the most distant galaxies in the Universe. Can you imagine what astronomers saw, or might see, through each of these breakthrough telescopes?

Hooker Telescope

Galileo Galilei

Activity 1.4: The Starry Messengers

Background to this Activity

Humans have been developing technology to help them study the heavens for centuries. In ancient times, structures like Egyptian obelisks and Mayan temples were built in orientation to repeating astronomical phenomena, illustrating a keen interest in and knowledge of celestial occurrences. As early as 220-150BCE, astrolabes were used to take very accurate measurements of the positions of stars and planets. However, it was not until the late 1500s that glassmaking and lens grinding technology was sufficiently developed to lead to the invention of the telescope.

While Galileo Galilei did not invent the telescope, he is credited with being the first person to use one to observe the night sky. Having heard about the 'Dutch perspective glass' invented by Hans Lippershey in 1608, Galileo went about making his own,

with a few improvements, which allowed him to magnify objects 20 times. Galileo's telescope enabled him to observe details of the heavens which had never been seen, including the rings of Saturn, Jupiter's four largest moons, and the planet Venus displaying phases just as the Moon does. His observations led him to conclude that the Sun was the centre of the Solar System as Copernicus had theorised, and not the Earth. He also studied shadows cast by mountains on the Moon and, using simple maths, proved they were similar to the mountains here on Earth.

Over time, larger telescopes were constructed which could collect and focus more light, and thereby provide more detailed views of the skies and allow fainter objects to be seen. The Hooker Telescope at the Mount Wilson Observatory in California, USA, was built in 1917 and, with a 2.5 metre primary mirror, was the world's largest telescope until 1949. Observations made in the 1920s by Edwin Hubble with this telescope led to two profound discoveries which revolutionised our understanding of the Universe. In 1923, his detailed observations of the Andromeda Galaxy proved that it lay outside of our own Milky Way, at a staggering distance of 2.5 million light years. In 1929, by combining information from

Resources Required

- Tablet or device to access Zap code (optional — see Useful Links)

Useful Links

Visit **discoverydiaries.org/ activities/the-starry-messengers** to download Zappar app content to use offline (PowerPoints, videos and image bundles etc.) and to access links to other info, which may be useful in planning and running this lesson.

observations of many distant galaxies, Hubble was able to show that the Universe is expanding as predicted by the Big Bang Theory. Both of these discoveries relied on the sensitivity and resolution of the Hooker Telescope.

As the 20th century progressed, humankind's ability to get clearer views of the heavens by making bigger telescopes ran up against a hard limit: the blurring effect of the Earth's atmosphere. Like a hazy view across a hot parking lot on a summer's day, views of space seen through Earth's atmosphere appear blurred as turbulent air bends light in different ways. The 1990 launch of the Hubble Space Telescope – named after Edwin Hubble – allowed us to observe space from above the atmosphere and gave us beautiful images of unprecedented resolution and sensitivity. A huge number of popular images of space have been taken by the Hubble Space Telescope; for people living today, this technology has fundamentally shaped our idea of 'what space looks like'. The telescope's capabilities have been updated by five servicing missions carried out by astronauts, and have produced ground-breaking discoveries about planets, stars, galaxies and the Universe.

The James Webb Space Telescope – or Webb – is a telescope for the next generation, which will shape our understanding of space just as the Hubble Space Telescope has. It will observe infrared light from space, and see things that Hubble can't.

For example, it will see through dusty nebulae (huge clouds of gas and dust) to make detailed pictures of forming stars and planets. It will detect the very first stars and galaxies ever formed in the Universe, over a distance of 13.4 billion light years. It will study the chemical compounds in the atmospheres of exoplanets – planets circling stars other than our Sun – and look for signs these planets might be habitable. While it has been specifically designed to do these amazing things, it will be used to study objects all over the sky. What's perhaps most exciting about Webb is its potential to show us things we can't now imagine, just as Galileo's telescope did over 400 years ago.

Running the Activity

Open by asking students to consider how we look at things that are far away on Earth. What instruments do we use to see in different ways? Prompt students to think about binoculars they may have used for sight-seeing or recreational activities like bird-watching. What different things can you learn by seeing things more clearly or by detecting things that are further away?

Have students list all the things they already know exist in space; you might use images of the Sun, Moon, planets, other moons, comets, nebulae and/or galaxies to prompt discussion, or you might ask students to find or draw these images. How many of these objects can/have students seen with their own eyes?

Got notes?
Write them
here!

How do we know they exist and what they look like? Have any students used telescopes before? What have they seen with them? What do they imagine they could see if they had access to a powerful telescope at an observatory? What about an observatory in space?

To help students understand why a telescope in space could humans give a clearer view, like the Hubble Space Telescope, ask them to think of looking across a hot parking lot and how the image seems wavy. You might use a simple demonstration of refraction – such as looking at a pencil in a glass half-filled with water – to help them understand that light is bent as it moves through different materials.

To understand why a telescope in space could see types of light that are blocked by the atmosphere, ask students to consider materials which are opaque/transparent to optical light and ask if they are also opaque/transparent to other types of light, such as ultraviolet light or radio waves. A good example is sunscreen – we can see through it, but it blocks harmful UV.

Once students have considered as a group how different telescopes allow us to learn more about space, introduce the four telescopes featured on the worksheet. Using the PowerPoint slides or Zap code materials provided, or through independent research, ask them to draw or collage a representation of what they might be able to see using each telescope.

Questions for the Class

- Why is it important to learn about space?
- What are some of the important discoveries that telescopes have made?
- What do you think Webb might discover about our Universe?
- What is the difference between a telescope, a space probe and a satellite?

Additional Challenges / Extension Activities

Create a detailed timeline about the history of the telescope using our selected references from STEM Learning — see Useful Links.

A fun craft activity that can help younger students understand the main components of a telescope, as well as how basic telescopes are used.

Ideas for Differentiation

Support:

- Work as a class or in small groups, using the visual prompts provided in the PowerPoint slides. Use a washing line to pin up key dates and changes in telescope discovery to support the students visually.

Challenge:

- Ask more capable students to research each telescopes' capabilities independently.

Teacher Tip!

Create a 'clothes peg' timeline in the classroom and add significant dates related to the development of the telescope.

DEEP SPACE QUIZ!

What have you learnt about the history of space observation? Create your own true or false quiz and test your friends!

True OR false?

Activity 1.5: The Deep Space Quiz

Background to this Activity

The Deep Space Quiz is a fun way for students to consolidate their learning from this chapter. Students can create a True/False quiz and use it to test their fellow classmates.

Running the Activity

Consolidate learning by inviting students to contribute what they've learnt. Note this down on a whiteboard, so that all students in the class can access the information. Revise any scientific vocabulary that students have encountered, along with the definitions of these words.

In groups or individually, ask students to prepare five questions, reminding them of the 'True/False' format. You may like to provide some examples of True/False questions by using the examples below, so that students understand the format their questions

must follow. Highlight the fact that 'False' questions are ones which do not accurately represent facts. Students may need time to research answers in order to better frame their questions.

Once students have prepared their questions, ask them to test each other in pairs, small groups or as a class.

True/False Sample Questions

- Nebulae, black holes, moons and solar winds are all found in deep space. / T

- Our Solar System is in a galaxy called the Murky Way. / F

- A constellation is a group of planets in the sky. / F

- Constellations appear to move in the sky because the Earth rotates on an axis. / T

- Mars is the planet closest to the Sun in our Solar System. / F

- Galileo was the first astronomer to theorise that Earth was the centre of our Solar System. / F

- Edwin Hubble used the Hooker Telescope to study our Universe. / T

- The Hubble Space Telescope discovered new moons orbiting Pluto. / T

Resources Required

- Tablet or device to access Zap code (optional — see Useful Links)

- Fact sheets/whiteboard paper from previous activities

Useful Links

Visit **discoverydiaries.org/ activities/the-deep-space-quiz** to access links to other info, which may be useful in planning and running this lesson.

- The James Webb Space Telescope (Webb) can see through space dust because of x-ray vision. / F
- The James Webb Telescope is positioned 1.5 million kilometres from Earth. / T

Questions for the Class

- Why is it important for scientists to ask questions?
- What are some questions you have about space that were not answered in Chapter 1?
- Are there any words in Chapter 1 that you don't understand? What are the different ways you could find out what they mean?
- Did you learn anything in Chapter 1 that amazed you?
- What are some of the ways we can learn more about the Universe without being astronauts?

Additional Challenges / Extension Activities

Host a game show, using questions written by students. To involve the whole class, use mini-whiteboards with T on one side and F on the other. Alternatively, replace the whiteboards with physical action, such as hands on heads for true and hands behind backs for false. This method will provide educators with instant feedback.

Ask students to rewrite their questions as full Q&As, rather than in a True/False format e.g. 'What are four things that are found in space?' or 'What is the name of the galaxy that our Solar System is in?'

Ideas for Differentiation

Support:

- Students create top trumps style Q&A cards to support recollection of learning.

Challenge:

- Ask students to research one question of their choice. Set them the challenge of proving why it is true or false and present their findings to the class.
- Provide students with a quota for True and False questions, such as three False questions, to ensure that they think creatively about the questions they formulate.

Teacher Tip!

Host a game show for the whole class by asking each student to contribute one of their true/false questions, then provide 'T' and 'F' signs for instant feedback.

Got notes? Write them here!

DON'T FORGET YOUR CLASSROOM INCENTIVES!

Award students MISSION BADGES as they finish each chapter

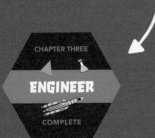

Hang a MISSION LOG POSTER in the classroom as part of a space display

Celebrate completing the programme with official certificates signed by Gillian Wright, Director of the UK Astronomy Technology Centre

Download free or purchase hardcopies of these resources at: DISCOVERYDIARIES.ORG

CHAPTER 2: TELESCOPE TRAINING

The first step to understanding how a telescope works is to learn about how light behaves. Students experiment with how light can be absorbed, reflected and split into the spectrum, before being introduced to light the human eye cannot see.

What's inside this chapter?

2.1 – Lights, Mirror, Action
Design a demonstration showing that light travels in straight lines, reflects off things and can be absorbed.
> Science + D&T

2.2 – Make-Your-Own Colour Wheel
Follow the instructions to make a colour wheel that turns the spectrum into white.
> Science + D&T

2.3 – Recipe for a Rainbow
Using a prism and light source, create a step-by-step guide on how to make a rainbow.
> Science + D&T

2.4 – Infrared Selfie
Create a colour scale representing cold to hot, then use it to draw a self-portrait.
> Science + Art

2.5 – Chapter Two Word Search
Find eight scientific words from Chapter Two.
> Science + Literacy

LIGHTS, MIRROR ACTION!

Light travels in a straight line. It can also reflect off things and create shadows. Can you design a demonstration to show people the wonder of light?

Plan and design your demonstration here

I want to show that...

☐ Light travels in a straight line

☐ Light can reflect off things

☐ Some materials absorb or block light

☐ add your own

Zap to explore the wonder of light!

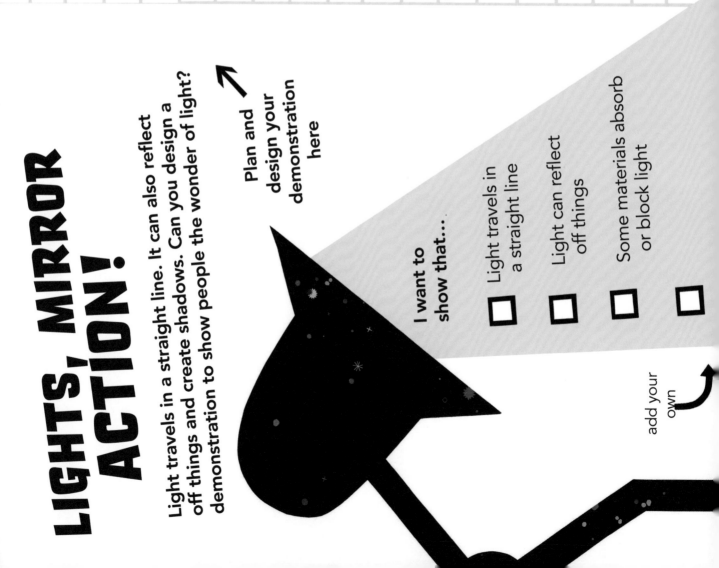

Activity 2.1: Lights, Mirror, Action

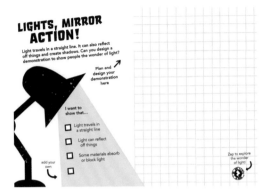

Risk Assessment

Ask students to consider the dangers of looking directly at light-sources (mainly the Sun) and how they can protect their eyes.

Background to this Activity

One of Webb's main goals is to observe galaxies that are billions of light years away, so that we can study how galaxies are formed. It does this by collecting light that's emitted from the stars in those galaxies. Because the light from these distant galaxies is very faint, Webb needs to collect as much as possible – the more light it collects, the more we can see. That's why its primary mirror is the largest ever to be sent to space – spanning 6.5 meters in diameter – more than double Hubble's primary mirror.

Webb's primary mirror is concave. When the light from space objects hits the primary mirror, the light is reflected from the mirror's golden surface into a more concentrated beam. This beam then hits the smaller convex secondary mirror, which reflects the light into the Webb's four special instruments. These instruments take pictures and also spread the light out into spectra. The information from the instruments is then digitised and sent back to Earth by radio link, so that scientists can study the observations.

Running the Activity

This activity asks students to plan, design and report on a demonstration which shows how light behaves.

Divide the class into small mixed ability groups. Provide each group with a selection of different items e.g. clear rulers/books/material/card etc, and a torch. Allow time for groups to discuss how they can use these resources to plan a demonstration of how light can reflect off things/absorb or block light/travel in straight lines.

Each group then feeds their ideas back to the class. This will provide all students with the opportunity to change or improve their demonstration.

Ensure that students understand the entire purpose of the task. At this point, you might want to provide

Resources Required

- Tablet or device to access Zap code (optional — see Useful Links)

- Drawing materials

- Torch (optional)

Useful Links

Visit **discoverydiaries.org/ activities/lights-mirror-action** to download Zappar app content to use offline (PowerPoints, videos and image bundles etc.) and to access links to other info, which may be useful in planning and running this lesson.

students with additional information regarding examples of ways to carry out the task. Students should make notes on the worksheet about how they will achieve their task.

Provide some examples if students are struggling to come up with ways to investigate e.g. arrange three pieces of card with holes punched in them in the same place, in an uneven line. Shine the torch at the cards; the light will stop and cannot travel through all three cards if they aren't in a straight line. Then arrange the cards in a straight line; the light can travel through.

Considering the range of items students have, ask students to rate the items on how well they allow light to pass through them/absorb or block light.

Students can use clean foil to see what happens when a torch is shined on it. Crumple up the foil; shine the torch on it. What happens now?

Allow students to experiment with mirrors. What happens if you put a mirror in front of another mirror? Ask students to write a word on a piece of paper and hold it in front of the mirror? What happens?

Questions for the Class

- What is light?
- Where does light come from?
- What is reflection?
- How are shadows created?

Additional Challenges / Extension Activities

Students could record and discuss their demonstration on an iPad/device.

Students can make their own periscope — see Useful Links.

Make shadow puppets and ask the students to experiment with how to make the shadows bigger and smaller. Record results in a table.

What is the best distance for a large, clear shadow?

Ask students to make observations when using concave or convex reflective surfaces, like those on a spoon. What happens to a reflection when a mirror isn't flat?

Got notes? Write them here!

_____

_____

_____

_____

_____

_____

_____

_____

Ideas for Differentiation

Support:

- For support, students could work in a guided group and be given suggested activities to use for their demonstration. They could then work independently to create and write up their plan and carry out their demonstration. For a greater challenge, students could include additional information on their plan and use scientific vocabulary.

Challenge:

- Students to be in mixed ability groupings.
- Students to be given ideas prompt cards to help scaffold their learning if needed.
- Students to include a detailed plan using scientific vocabulary.

Teacher Tip!

Do this activity outside on a sunny day! Using sunlight, students can experiment with reflective materials like mirrors as well as materials that absorb light and cast shadows.

MAKE-YOUR-OWN COLOUR WHEEL

It's time to put your maths and engineering skills to the test. Can you show how colour turns to white?

What you will need:

- ☐ Cardboard
- ☐ White paper
- ☐ Compass
- ☐ Protractor
- ☐ Scissors
- ☐ Glue
- ☐ Coloured pencils
- ☐ String

Zap to watch a how-to video

Step One: Use a compass to draw a circle with a 100mm diameter onto the paper.

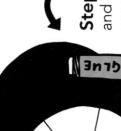

Step Two: Use your protractor to divide the circle into 7 equal sections. What equation will you use to work out the size of the sections?

___ ÷ ___ = ___

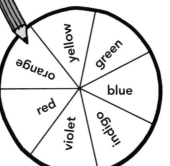

Step Three: Colour each section as shown, then cut out the circle.

yellow, green, blue, indigo, violet, red, orange

Step Four: Draw a 100mm circle on the cardboard and cut out.

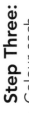

Step Five: Glue the paper and card circles together and use your compass to make **two** holes in the middle.

Step Six: Feed the string through the holes as shown or invent your own spinning mechanism!

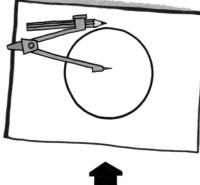

Step Seven: Spin and observe! What do you notice? Describe your observations here.

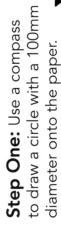

Activity 2.2: Make-Your-Own Colour Wheel

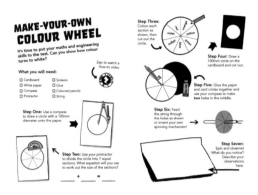

Background to this Activity

This activity allows students to explore how white light is made up of colours, and therefore how it can be split into the spectrum. It will prepare students for the activities in Chapter 5, which introduces the concept of spectroscopy and how this science can be used to help us learn about the Universe, with the help of telescopes like Webb.

Running the Activity

Begin by reviewing what students know about the light spectrum. Ask students questions about colour: what different colours are there? Can you combine colours and what happens if you do combine them? If available, use filters to demonstrate how combining different colours can have different results.

Next, ask students: what colour is light? Discuss – this could be made more interactive by having pieces of paper around the room (the seven colours of the rainbow and white) and asking students to move to the space near the colour they think is light.

You don't need to tell students the answer at this stage but can tell them you will return to this question at the end of the lesson.

Ask students: how many colours are in a rainbow? Make links to rainbows and ask for suggestions about how the colours of the spectrum can be remembered e.g. a mnemonic like Richard Of York Gave Battle In Vain.

Explain that the task of the lesson is to make a colour wheel to explore what happens when the colours in the spectrum are mixed.

Gather resources and follow the instructions on the worksheet.

At the end of the session, ask the question: What colours make white light? Through discussion, guide students to the conclusion that white light is made up of the colours of the spectrum.

Solution to this Activity

The equation to be used in Step Two is:

$360 \div 7 = 51$ (rounded to the nearest whole number)

Resources Required

- Tablet or device to access Zap code (optional — see Useful Links)
- Cardboard
- White paper
- Compass and protractor
- Scissors
- Glue
- Coloured pencils or paint
- String

Questions for the Class

- What are the colours in the spectrum?

- How can we remember these?

- What colours make up white light?

- When do we see the different colours of light in nature?

- CHALLENGE: Are these the only colours in the spectrum? Why do you think this?

- CHALLENGE: Why do we see the colours of the spectrum in a rainbow?

Additional Challenges / Extension Activities

Make your own spectrometer — see Useful Links.

Explore why the sky is blue. Follow the instructions and demonstration here — see Useful Links.

Ideas for Differentiation

Support:

- Circles could be provided rather than require students to draw and cut out their own circles.

- Lines could be pre-marked on the circles if students do not have experience in using a protractor (angle measurer).

Challenge:

- Students could be given a template to draw around to create a circle instead of using a pair of compasses.

- Students could be given the angle they need to draw if they struggle to use a protractor accurately.

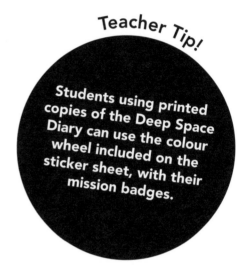

Teacher Tip!

Students using printed copies of the Deep Space Diary can use the colour wheel included on the sticker sheet, with their mission badges.

Useful Links

Visit **discoverydiaries.org/ activities/make-your-own- colour-wheel** to download Zappar app content to use offline (PowerPoints, videos and image bundles etc.) and to access links to other info, which may be useful in planning and running this lesson.

Got notes? Write them here!

RECIPE FOR A RAINBOW

A colour wheel turns colour into white, but how can we turn white light into colour? In other words, how do we make a rainbow? The ingredients are simple – light and a prism. But how exactly do we cook up a rainbow from that? Create a step-by-step guide and don't forget to include a colourful diagram!

Zap to explore the colour spectrum!

Activity 2.3: Recipe for a Rainbow

Background to this Activity

The James Webb Space Telescope uses the light collected by its huge primary mirror to help us learn about distant stars. Some of its specialist instruments split the light into spectra, which astronomers use to discover more about objects in space, such as what they are made of. Specifically, Webb sees light in the infrared region of the spectrum. The human eye cannot detect these wavelengths (for example, we cannot see light emitted from a remote control we use to change the channel on a TV), so we need specialist instruments like those on Webb to detect and study what would otherwise be invisible.

Infrared was first discovered by Frederick William Herschel in 1738, when he split light through a prism to form a spectrum and then measured the temperature of each colour. He then measured the temperature next to the red light – where there appeared to be no colour – and found it was even hotter than any colours in the spectrum. Following this discovery, Herschel went on to prove that this invisible light – which came to be known as infrared – refracted and reflected the same way that sunlight did. Infrared light is explored in Activity 2.4: Infrared Selfie. The scientific technique of splitting light into the spectrum is called spectroscopy. Astronomers use spectroscopy to learn about the properties of stars.

Following on from Activity 2.1: Lights, Mirror, Action and Activity 2.2: Make-Your-Own Colour Wheel, this activity provides students with the opportunity to learn – or revisit – how prisms and other objects can be used to split white light into those colours. It has been designed to be as open as possible, so educators can adapt it to their available resources and their students' existing knowledge.

Running the Activity

Gauge the level of understanding within the class. Students should know that light travels in straight lines and, having explored colour wheels, should have an idea that white light is made up of a spectrum of colours.

Resources Required

- Tablet or device to access Zap code (optional — see Useful Links)
- White paper or surfaces
- Torches and other light sources
- A range of prisms

Useful Links

Visit discoverydiaries.org/activities/recipe-for-a-rainbow to download Zappar app content to use offline (PowerPoints, videos and image bundles etc.) and to access links to other info, which may be useful in planning and running this lesson.

Provide students with a variety of resources and allow time for them to discuss (in pairs and small groups prior to whole class discussion) how they might explore the idea of showing the colours in the light spectrum.

Resources should, ideally, include:

- white paper or surfaces
- torches and other light sources
- a range of prisms.

If you do not have access to prisms, the experiment can be carried out using crystals and bright sunlight, which will show the colours on a pale surface. You could also have images of rainbows, oil spills on wet roads and bubbles showing the colours of the spectrum.

Students should be encouraged to consider for themselves how they might go about splitting white light from a torch (or other light sources).

Students can record in different ways what they plan to do and what they predict is going to happen. They should be encouraged to work scientifically, selecting the equipment and recording the process using diagrams and labels, as well as numbered and/or bullet pointed lists.

Solution to this Activity

This very short clip explains how the prism causes the light to be refracted (rather than reflected) — see Useful Links.

It also includes a simple demonstration of how students could set up their own experiment to split white light into a spectrum to show the colours of the rainbow.

Questions for the Class

- How have you shown the different colours contained in white light?
- How many colours have you managed to split white light into?
- Can you describe what has happened to the light as it has travelled through the prism?
- Where do we see these colours together in the natural world?

Additional Challenges / Extension Activities

Explore the idea of refraction.

Investigate the wavelength bands of the spectrum and represent them on a graph or visually.

Explore invisible light by investigating UV. Conduct an experiment with UV beads, or contact your local STEM ambassador for more ideas. See Useful Links.

Ideas for Differentiation

Support:

- Provide only one type of light source and one type of prism to guide students when creating their own experiments.

Got notes?
Write them
here!

Challenge:

- Provide a range of resources, some of which are not particularly relevant, to enable students to develop the skills to identify what is useful and what is not.

- Ask students to explore the idea that there could be more than seven colours in the light spectrum.

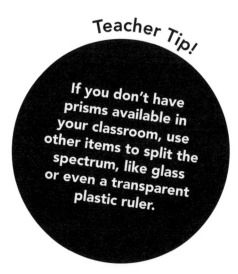

Teacher Tip!

If you don't have prisms available in your classroom, use other items to split the spectrum, like glass or even a transparent plastic ruler.

INFRARED SELFIE!

Imagine being able to see things that are invisible. The Webb telescope will reveal new things about the Universe by detecting infrared light. This is a type of light which our eyes can't see, like ultraviolet light which causes sunburn. Our bodies can detect infrared light as heat. Draw a self-portrait in infrared and see what it reveals about you!

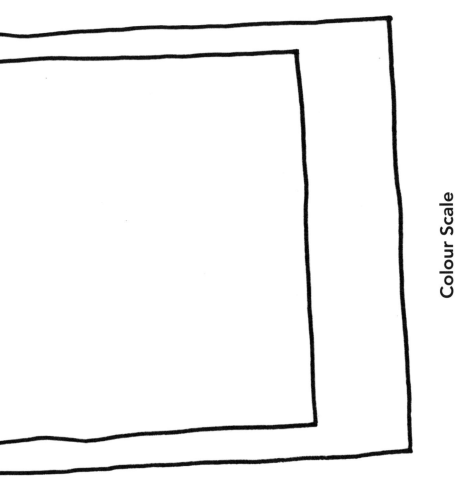

Hi space observer!

I'm Martyn Wells, an optical engineer working on Webb. Let's see what you look like in infrared. Create a colour scale that represents cold to hot, using any colours you like. Then draw your portrait using these colours to show the parts of your face that are hotter and cooler.

Zap to see
infrared pictures
then draw your own!

Colour Scale

cold — hot

Activity 2.4: Infrared Selfie!

Background to this Activity

The James Webb Space Telescope detects infrared light, which can penetrate thick clouds of space dust. This means that with Webb, we can see things that are otherwise hidden, like protostars (baby stars).

Infrared is a form of light that human eyes can't see but which we can feel as heat. Everything in the Universe that is warm – from stars and planets to animals, microbes and even non-living things like a lump of charcoal – emits thermal radiation/light. How much thermal radiation they emit depends on how hot they are. The majority of thermal radiation for things of 'normal' temperature are in the infrared spectrum, meaning they will be detected by infrared (IR) cameras, like those on Webb.

Infrared technology can also tell us about the temperature of the object. Generally, the settings on IR cameras will depict hot objects (or regions/areas/parts) as bright and cold objects (or regions/areas/parts) as dark. Thermal-imaging cameras, such as night-vision cameras, use infrared technology.

Before conducting the activity, ask your school administration if they have an IR camera for thermal testing. Alternatively, schools in Scotland can borrow a thermal camera from their local authorities, for in-class demonstrations. For more information about this scheme, contact SSERC — see Useful Links.

Running the Activity

Students should have prior knowledge of portraiture and be familiar with blending techniques using colouring pencils. Students will need a selection of colouring pencils for this task. Students can base their colour scale on a traditional cold to hot/blue to red scale, or they can invent their own scale.

Begin by asking students if any of them know what 'infrared light' is. Ask them if they know any other forms of light (visible light, ultraviolet (UV) light etc). Tell them that some animals can see different wavelengths of light that we can't see (bees can see UV light and snakes can see IR light). TV remotes use infrared light which we can't

Resources Required

- Tablet or device to access Zap code (optional — see Useful Links)

- Colouring pencils

Useful Links

Visit **discoverydiaries.org/activities/infrared-selfie** to download Zappar app content to use offline (PowerPoints, videos and image bundles etc.) and to access links to other info, which may be useful in planning and running this lesson.

see but this can be picked up on some phone cameras. (If you point the remote at the camera and press a button, you may see the bright infrared beam through the phone screen but not with your own eyes.)

Look at the example provided by the iTunes link in Useful Links and discuss how infrared has been used in space research. Pause the footage at 2min 45s to discuss the various features on the presenter's face. As a class, discuss the colour range within the infrared camera (from black through to bright white and moving through a spectrum of blue, purple, red, orange, yellow as temperature increases). Have students colour in the colour scale bar either to represent this, or ask them to create their own scale from cold to hot.

When everyone has created their scale, it will be time to introduce students to infrared images. Start by showing them some images of animals, taken with an infrared camera (see Useful Links). Note which animals have fur and which don't. How do these images compare? What differences do students notice when an animal is warm-blooded or cold-blooded? And what happens if a person is wearing glasses, that block infrared light?

Students can now begin drawing their selfies. Establish the relatively warm and cool parts of their face. Ask students to think about which

parts of their faces are warmer than others. Typically, ears and noses will be cooler and eyelids, mouths and lips will be warmer. Using their fingertips, can students detect which areas of their faces are warmer and cooler? Once students have spent some time exploring, they can then use this information to sketch out their face and begin to shade it with their colouring pencils, carefully blending from cool to warm through the spectrum of colours in their scale. Students who wear glasses can choose how they represent themselves. Other students might like to draw themselves wearing sunglasses.

At the end of the lesson, ask students what they have learnt about infrared light.

Questions for the Class

- What type of light can humans see?
- What other types of light are there?
- How can infrared light help us in the study of space?
- Based on the colour scale a student has chosen, what colour would something cool show up as on an infrared camera? What about something warm?

Additional Challenges / Extension Activities

Explore infrared light through this experiment — see Useful Links.

Got notes? Write them here!

Ideas for Differentiation

Support:

- Create the colour scale together and model the task on the board.

- Demonstrate blending techniques and allow students to practise blending colours together before they start.

Challenge:

- Students create the colour spectrum more independently, with less teacher input.

- Students could use watercolour pencils.

Teacher Tip!

Infrared light can be a difficult concept for young learners to understand so liken it to ultraviolet light, which we can't see but which causes sunburn.

CHAPTER TWO
WORD SEARCH

Zap for the answers!

Find the words you've learnt in this chapter and add them to your Visual Dictionary of Deep Space at the back of the book.
Words can go forward, backward and diagonally.

L	B	G	I	S	K	N	S	I	T
A	R	Q	L	I	U	P	G	N	C
C	O	H	O	F	E	R	P	F	E
I	S	P	S	C	A	R	P	R	L
T	B	R	T	D	M	P	L	A	F
P	A	R	I	Q	I	D	X	R	E
O	U	E	L	I	G	H	T	E	R
M	N	F	W	Z	I	O	K	D	S
T	C	J	T	Q	U	E	C	Q	B
X	K	D	F	I	X	S	U	I	V
P	R	I	S	M	Q	J	T	J	Y

Target = 8 words beginning with:

A L R G O S I P

Chapter Two: Word Search

CHAPTER TWO
WORD SEARCH

Zap for the answers!

Find the words you've learnt in this chapter and add them to your Visual Dictionary of Deep Space at the back of the book. Words can go forward, backward and diagonally.

Target = 8 words beginning with:

A L R G O S I P

Background to this Activity

Word searches are a fun way to build your students' vocabularies. You can extend these activities with the Visual Dictionary of Deep Space (see below).

Running the Activity

The word searches provide an opportunity to review and discuss what has been covered in each chapter. For each word search, look at the starting letters noted below the word search grid. As a class or in student pairs, discuss what some of the words might be. Ask students if they can identify any of those words.

As students complete the word searches, remind them to write new words in their Visual Dictionary of Deep Space (see Activity 6.2).

Solutions to this Activity

**CHAPTER TWO
WORD SEARCH**

Zap for the answers!

Find the words you've learnt in this chapter and add them to your Visual Dictionary of Deep Space at the back of the book. Words can go forward, backward and diagonally.

Target = 8 words beginning with:
A L R G O S I P

Word Search Chapter 2: Absorb, Light, Reflect, Gradient, Optical, Spectrum, Infrared, Prism

Definitions:

Absorb: to take in or soak up by chemical or physical action

Light: that which stimulates sight and makes things visible

Resources Required

- Rulers
- Computers, devices or textbooks for research
- Pens/Pencils
- Visual Dictionary of Deep Space
- Tablet or device to access Zap code (optional — see Useful Links)

Useful Links

Visit **discoverydiaries.org/activities/ chapter-two-word-search** to download Zappar app content to use offline (PowerPoints, videos and image bundles etc.) and to access links to other info, which may be useful in planning and running this lesson.

Reflect: to bounce light without absorbing it

Gradient: a slope; the degree to which something (e.g. a line or surface) slopes above or below a horizontal plane; an increase or decrease in the magnitude of something (temperature, brightness)

Optical: relating to sight, especially in relation to the action of light; falling in the part of the spectrum which the human eye can see

Spectrum: the separation of light according to wavelength, part of which can be seen by human eyes as a band of colours

Infrared: light beyond the red end of the visible spectrum, which can't be seen but can be felt as heat

Prism: a glass or other transparent object in the form of a prism

Ideas for Differentiation

Support:

- Work as a class or in groups to find definitions, assigning words to students.

- Work as a class or in groups to create a song using vocabulary from the chapter.

- Provide hidden words to students.

Challenge:

- Once students have completed the word searches, ask them to develop their own. Photocopy the blank word search template on page 18 or download and print a template (see Useful Links). Students can then test a classmate with their word search. Differentiate by giving clues as the whole word, the first letter or a definition of the word.

Teacher Tip!

As an additional challenge, ask students to put the solutions in alphabetical order.

Got notes? Write them here!

CHAPTER 3:
DESIGNING FOR DISCOVERY

The James Webb Space Telescope is a complex feat of
science and engineering. Using its unique design as a
basis, students develop their maths, science and D&T
skills to create their own space telescope, then prepare
it for deployment.

What's inside this chapter?

3.1 – Blueprint for Space
Complete the dot-to-dot by solving the maths equations, then use
the key to unveil Webb's structure.
> Science + Maths

3.2 – Mega Mirror Engineer
Find the lines of symmetry in the provided shapes, then design a mirror
that meets the engineering brief.
> Science + Maths

3.3 – Keep it Cool
Design an experiment to test how effectively different materials act
as conductors and insulators.
> Science + Maths

3.4 – Pack Your Payload
Using only the provided deployment mechanisms, design a model
of Webb that folds into its rocket.
> Science + D&T

3.5 – Chapter Three Word Search
Find eight scientific words from Chapter Three.
> Science + Literacy

BLUEPRINT FOR SPACE

It's time to unveil the blueprint for your space telescope. Each dot in this puzzle has a sum beside it. Start by completing the sums then join the dots according to the key below.

Zap to reveal Webb's blueprint

1 x 1 =

12 ÷ 4 =

25 ÷ 5 =

21 - 19 =

12 - 8 =

18 ÷ 3 =

4 x 4 =

21 ÷ 3 =

42 - 28 =

7 + 5 =

100 ÷ 10 =

50 - 42 =

KEY	
Antenna	Even Numbers
Sunshield	
Primary Mirror	Odd Numbers
Mirror Support Structure	
Control System	

Some components are missing a visual key. Can you colour them in on the diagram and add the colour to the key?

Activity 3.1: Blueprint for Space

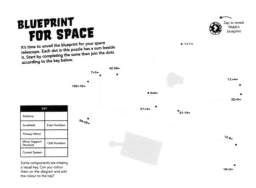

Background to this Activity

This activity helps students understand the James Webb Space Telescope's structure while explaining its 'hot and cold' sides.

Webb has a unique structure, especially when compared with other space telescopes which are often cylindrical with long solar panels. Webb's gold-coated hexagonal primary mirror, mounted in the centre of its silver-coloured sunshield, gives it a striking appearance.

The main features of the Webb are:

Primary mirror: the distinctive gold mirror, made of 18 hexagonal segments. The primary mirror collects infrared light from objects in space.

Secondary mirror: this smaller mirror is positioned to face the primary mirror, reflecting collected light into Webb's scientific instruments.

Scientific instruments (not shown on worksheet): Webb's four instruments – which include cameras and spectrographs – are housed in the Science Instrument Module, which sits behind the primary mirror.

Sunshield: the kite-shaped sunshield is roughly the size of a tennis court and it plays a crucial role for Webb. It shields Webb's mirrors and science instruments from the heat and light of the Sun, Earth and Moon, keeping the telescope very cold. In order to detect the faint infrared light emitted by distant space objects, Webb's optics and instruments must be protected from any other sources of heat – including the telescope itself. The sunshield is made of five layers of shiny, silver material with gaps in-between them, to reflect and disperse heat. Through passive cooling, the sunshield keeps Webb's cool side at a temperature of lower than –200 degrees Celsius.

Solar panels (not shown on worksheet): Webb's solar panels provide the telescope with power by converting sunlight into electricity. They are positioned to always face the Sun.

Spacecraft control system: this component houses Webb's steering and control machinery, including its computer.

Resources Required

- Tablet or device to access Zap code (optional — see Useful Links)
- Rulers

Useful Links

Visit **discoverydiaries.org/ activities/blueprint-for-space** to download Zappar app content to use offline (PowerPoints, videos and image bundles etc.) and to access links to other info, which may be useful in planning and running this lesson.

Antenna: the Earth-pointing antenna is Webb's link to Earth. It sends scientific data to Earth and receives commands from Mission Control.

Webb has a 'hot side' and a 'cold side'. Its sunshield can be likened to a beach umbrella or parasol, separating the two sides. Webb's hot side faces the Sun and includes everything that is in front of the sunshield: the solar panels, the control system and the antenna. Everything behind the sunshield forms the cold side: the primary and secondary mirrors, and the Science Instrument Module.

In order to observe space, Webb's specialist instruments must be kept at a very cold temperature. The sunshield keeps the cold side of Webb at a temperature of -234 degrees Celsius – cold enough to ensure that it won't emit infrared light. Three of Webb's four instruments can detect light from space objects at this temperature. The fourth instrument – the Mid-Infrared Instrument (MIRI) – must be kept at an even colder temperature to function properly. To achieve this, engineers have created a special cryocooler – essentially a space refrigerator! – for MIRI, which keeps it at -266 degrees Celsius. MIRI is attached to the Science Instrument Module with special insulating carbon struts designed to avoid heat transfer. Activity 3.3: Space Lab (see Useful Links) explores cooling and insulation further.

Running the Activity

Start by asking the class for examples of how we protect ourselves from the Sun (e.g. sunscreen, sunglasses, hats, UV protection clothing, seeking shade or staying indoors during the hottest parts of the day, using umbrellas at the beach). Explain to students that this activity is about the structure of Webb, and how its design protects it from the Sun.

Using the background information above, discuss Webb's structure with students. Read as a class (or pick individuals to read) information about the main features of Webb and ask students if they can identity the different components. Use the image 'Basic Structure 1' as a prompt – see Useful Links.

Once students have guessed which component is which, they can check their responses against the image 'Basic Structure 2' – see Useful Links.

Explain to students that Webb has hot and cold sides on either side of its sunshield, just as a beach umbrella does. Show the class a picture of a tennis court to explain that this is the size of the sunshield – see Useful Links.

Ask students to study the telescope and discuss with a partner (or as a class) what they notice. For each of Webb's components, can they guess

Got notes? Write them here!

_____

_____

_____

_____

_____

_____

_____

_____

_____

whether that component sits on the hot or cold side?

Ask the questions below. Students to discuss with a partner and feedback to the class.

Explain to students that they are going to unveil the blueprint for the telescope.

Discuss the term 'key' and allow students to explore the different components of Webb listed on the key, matching it to the blueprint. To check the students understanding of the key, ask them to find and trace their finger over the control system, antenna and the primary mirror. Once they have familiarised themselves with the components, they can create their key.

Explain that they will be working out two sets of numbers – odd and even. Recap what the difference is and what types of numbers they will be looking for. Ensure that students understand that the purpose of the task is to work out the sums, record the answers and then join up the dots according to the key (odds and evens).

See Useful Links below for images of Webb showing its hot and cold sides.

Solutions to the Activity

Sums for the sunshield/even numbers equal: 2, 4, 6, 8, 10, 12, 14 and 16

Sums for the secondary mirror and support structure equal: 1, 3, 5 and 7

Questions for the Class

- What stands out for you about the telescope?
- Why do you think the hot side of the telescope has been named this?
- What do you notice about the mirrors positioning on the telescope? (Try to draw out from the children the sunshield helps to stop the heat from the Sun.)
- Where are solar panels? What do solar panels do? Do you think the solar panels are on the hot side or the cold side of Webb? Why?

Additional Challenges / Extension Activities

Investigate which sides of Webb are hot and cold, and find out the temperature ranges they can withstand.

Design Webb on the computer and label it.

Film a one-minute news report discussing Webb and answering questions about it.

Create a fact file about any interesting facts about Webb.

Ideas for Differentiation

Support:

- Students to work with a partner or in small groups to answer the mathematical questions

- Students to record each number on the line

- Differentiate by providing solutions; students to join up the dots (odds or evens) from the smallest to largest

Challenge:

- Students to work independently/ with a partner to answer the mathematical questions

- Can students add any other details to the blueprint?

  - Label the hot side and cold side of Webb

  - Label the temperature range of each side

  - Using arrows, show the direction light of the Sun

- Can students come up with their own sums for the dot-to-dot solutions?

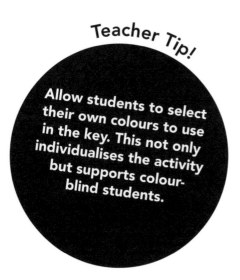

Teacher Tip!

Allow students to select their own colours to use in the key. This not only individualises the activity but supports colour-blind students.

MEGA MIRROR ENGINEER

A space telescope needs a big mirror, called the primary mirror, to collect lots of light and reflect it into its special instruments. The best way to do this is by using a symmetrical mirror. **Can you design one, according to the engineering brief below?**

Hi space explorer, I'm Piyal Samara-Ratna, a mechanical engineer, and I have an engineering challenge for you. Can you design a mirror that is **symmetrical**, made of **19 shapes** in total and has **no gaps** between segments so we don't lose any precious light?

Compare your design to Webb's primary mirror!

Start by drawing the lines of symmetry through these shapes:

 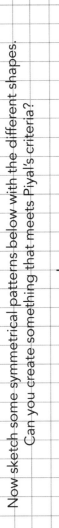

Now sketch some symmetrical patterns below with the different shapes. Can you create something that meets Piyal's criteria?

Line of Symmetry

Activity 3.2: Mega Mirror Engineer

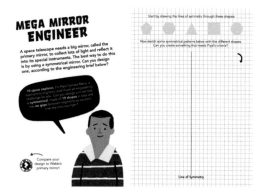

Background to this Activity

The James Webb Space Telescope's striking primary mirror makes it instantly recognisable. Hexagonal in shape, it spans 6.5 metres at its widest point, which is more than double the size of Hubble's primary mirror (Hubble's circular mirror is 2.4 metres in diameter). The bigger a telescope's mirror, the more light it can collect. The more light collected means the more we can see.

Webb's mirror is made up of 19 smaller hexagons which are all the same size. Eighteen of these are mirrors, called segments. The segments are arranged around the optical system at the centre of the mirror, which accounts for the 19th hexagon. Using hexagons means that there are no gaps between the segments, so none of the light hitting the mirror is lost. Each segment of the primary mirror can be adjusted

to focus the light that hits it onto the smaller secondary mirror. The secondary mirror then directs the light to Webb's science instruments.

Webb's primary mirror is coated in an extremely thin layer of gold, giving it its distinctive colour. The gold coating improves the mirror's reflection of infrared light.

Running the Activity

Open the lesson by asking students the questions: what do mirrors do (reflect light), and why we use them in telescopes (to collect more light than we can see with our eyes)? As a class, discuss different types of mirrors and what happens to our reflection if we look into mirrors that aren't flat, e.g. a spoon.

Ask students to think about the shape of different telescope mirrors. Are they familiar with any telescope mirrors? Do they have any ideas about why the mirrors are shaped the way they are?

Explain that this lesson is about Webb's primary mirror. In designing the mirror, engineers had to ensure that it was light-weight, strong and able to fold up into a compact configuration for launch. They also wanted it to be roughly circular and symmetrical, so it

Resources Required

- Tablet or device to access Zap code (optional — see Useful Links)
- Rulers

Useful Links

Visit **discoverydiaries.org/ activities/mega-mirror-engineer** to download Zappar app content to use offline (PowerPoints, videos and image bundles etc.) and to access links to other info, which may be useful in planning and running this lesson.

could produce images without complicated distortions.

Explain to students that the mirror they will design needs to be symmetrical. Ask students to explain what that means. Look at the 2-D shapes on the worksheet and ask students to draw the lines of symmetry for each. Ask them to investigate which shapes have the most lines of symmetry.

Remind students that their task is to design the mirror making sure it is symmetrical. This activity isn't about getting the mirror design the same as Webb's, rather, the focus should be on using the criteria of being symmetrical to generate possibilities and solutions. Students can use the space on the page to try out different symmetrical patterns with some or all of the different shapes.

Use the shapes templates provided with this activity (see Useful Links) to allow students to test out some different designs, before thinking about the final design they want to choose. The shapes can be downloaded from the website and photocopied.

At the end of the activity look at the design that Webb's engineers decided on and ask students to compare their designs with it (see Useful Links for diagrams). Visit the activity's webpage to view a clip that will give students an understanding of the process involved in constructing the mirror. For support, you could show this clip to the class before they begin their designs. Alternatively, show it to the class after they have completed their designs, so they can compare their designs to that of Webb's.

Questions for the Class

- What is the purpose of the primary mirror?

- Why is it important for a telescope to collect as much light as possible?

- What shape is Webb's primary mirror?

- What are some of the reasons that engineers chose this shape?

- Why is the mirror made up of smaller segments?

Additional Challenges / Extension Activities

Draw some further 'mirror designs' with a line of symmetry for a classmate to complete.

Investigate other primary mirrors used in telescopes such as the Extremely Large Telescope or the Hubble Space Telescope.

Draw patterns with further shapes (e.g. octagons) to see if they can create different mirror designs.

Got notes? Write them here!

73

Ideas for Differentiation

Support:

- Provide students with a design for them to reflect on.

Challenge:

- Explain to students that more lines of symmetry result in a better quality telescope. Ask students to look for multiple lines of symmetry in different mirror designs beyond the given vertical line, including horizontal and diagonal lines.

- Use more criteria for drawing the design (e.g. no right angles).

Teacher Tip!

Support students by downloading the shapes templates from discoverydiaries.org and allowing students to experiment with different design options. You'll find the templates under 'Extras' on the activity page.

KEEP IT COOL

The infrared camera is the "eye" of your telescope. It needs to be extremely cold to work properly. Can you experiment with different ways to keep it cool? Which methods might work in space?

Draw and label a diagram of your experiment.

I want to find out...

I will need the following materials:

My method will be to:

I predict...

Activity 3.3: Keep it Cool

KEEP IT COOL

The infrared camera is the "eye" of your telescope. It needs to be extremely cold to work properly. Can you experiment with different ways to keep it cool? Which methods might work in space?

Draw and label a diagram of your experiment.

I want to find out...

I will need the following materials:

My method will be to:

I predict...

Risk Assessment

If using ice and/or warm water in this activity, please conduct a risk assessment prior to running the activity, according to your school or institution's guidelines and procedures.

Background to this Activity

This activity explores different ways of keeping objects cool.

It is a common misconception that space is uniformly very cold. While some parts of space are very cold – like Neptune which has an average temperature of -214 degrees Celsius – other parts of space will be very hot. For example, if we measured the temperature outside the International Space Station, which orbits Earth beyond our protective atmosphere, it would be around 150 degrees Celsius on the side facing the Sun.

Temperature of objects in space is determined by many factors, including whether they create their own heat and light, their distance from other sources of heat and light, how reflective they are, and the presence and characteristics of an atmosphere. For example, despite being further away from the Sun than Mercury, Venus is a hotter planet due to its thick atmosphere.

The James Webb Space Telescope has a 'hot' and 'cold' side, as explored in Activity 3.1: Blueprint for Space. The hot side, which faces the Sun, reaches a temperature of 80 degrees Celsius. The cold side is kept at a temperature of -233 degrees Celsius by Webb's sunshield, which reflects and disperses heat.

The Mid-Infrared Instrument, or MIRI, is one of Webb's special instruments. It detects infrared light emitted by objects in space, and creates images and spectra of those objects so scientists can study them. In order for MIRI to capture infrared light, it must be kept at -266 degrees Celsius, which

Resources Required

- Tablet or device to access Zap code (optional — see Useful Links)
- Ice cubes
- Thermometers
- Clocks/timing devices
- A variety of materials including tinfoil/something reflective, insulating materials like cotton wool/fabric/cardboard, etc
- Other construction/D&T materials
- Clear plastic cups/containers/beakers
- Cardboard – to make lids (which can also be insulated) if desirable
- Warm water – could be an alternative to measure how quickly it cools if no easy access to ice (optional)

is thirty degrees cooler than the other instruments. Because of this, engineers have developed a cryogenic cooling system specifically for MIRI.

This investigation allows students to explore how materials can act as insulators and conductors. Students can trial a range of materials and use them to insulate an ice cube, measuring heat loss. This will allow them to draw conclusions about the most effective insulator. The activity is designed to focus on the scientific enquiry aspect, making this accessible to all age groups.

Running the Activity

Discuss why it is hot and cold in different parts of space, and why it is important to protect Webb's scientific instruments from the Sun's heat. Following this discussion, ask students to conduct an experiment to answer the question: which materials provide the best protection from heat?

Students design their own method to conduct their investigation.

A simple method to follow for support:

- Choose three different materials which insulate.
- Put ice cubes in three plastic or glass cups/containers/beakers. Students to decide on the number of ice cubes or mass of ice cubes. If you are working with older students, you could have a discussion here around the importance of control variables.

- Cover each cup with a different material – this could be as a lid, around the container or both.
- Position the cups so they are below a heat source e.g. Sun/windowsill/lamp.
- At intervals (students to decide suitable time interval – to support, teacher to suggest 15 seconds, 30 seconds, 60 seconds – students to choose) record the temperatures on the surface of the materials facing the heat source and at the bottom of each cup.
- Record results in the provided table.
- Students can visualise this as a graph.

Solutions to the Activity

Students to draw their own conclusions.

Suggested materials that are readily available: Cotton wool, cardboard, bubble wrap, cloth, paper, plastic, tinfoil, rubber, foam.

A time interval that works best is usually 60 seconds.

When drawing conclusions, the slower the ice cube melts (heats up) the better the insulator.

A scientific conclusion model:

Our best insulator was (insert name of material) as the temperature of the ice showed the slowest increase. This shows that the heat loss was the slowest, or reduced the most by the insulating material. At the beginning of each experiment, the temperature of the ice was (insert temperature)

Got notes? Write them here!

_____
_____
_____
_____
_____
_____
_____

and over (insert time period –
5 minutes) it increased by (insert
temperature increase) to (insert final
temperature reading).

Questions for the Class

- What are conductors?

- What are insulators?

- Why is it important to understand
the different properties of materials?

- How can we use this knowledge of
insulators to help us in everyday life?

Additional Challenges /
Extension Activities

Students to explore the following
questions to extend their scientific
thinking:

- Can students plot a graph to show
their results?

- Can students plan next steps to their
investigation?

- What questions have arisen from this
experiment?

If available, use an infrared camera
to observe how heat is lost during
the experiment, comparing different
types of insulation students have
used. Ask your school administration
if they have an IR camera for thermal
testing. Alternatively, schools in
Scotland can borrow thermal cameras
from their local authorities. For more
information about this scheme,
contact SSERC (www.sserc.org.uk).

Ideas for Differentiation

Support:

- Use the support frames for
conclusion/table of results.

- How can we apply this knowledge
to making spacesuit to keep an
astronaut warm?

Challenge:

- Use the extension questions to
challenge thinking.

- Can they test conductors? Which
increase the rate of heat loss?

Useful Links

Visit **discoverydiaries.org/
activities/keep-it-cool** to
download Zappar app content
to use offline (PowerPoints,
videos and image bundles etc.)
and to access links to other info,
which may be useful in planning
and running this lesson.

Teacher Tip!

If you're able to run
experiments in class,
the Deep Space Diary
Teacher Toolkit includes a
Table of Results template
where students can
record their temperature
measurements over time.

PACK YOUR PAYLOAD

Engineers are trying to find a way to fit Webb into the Ariane 5 rocket. Using only paper, glue and scissors, design a model of the telescope that folds to fit into the rocket's payload bay.

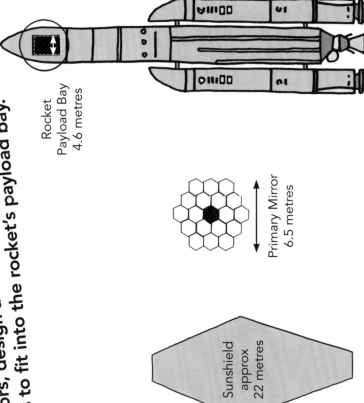

Rocket
Payload Bay
4.6 metres

Primary Mirror
6.5 metres

Sunshield
approx
22 metres

Your model must only use these five deployment mechanisms:

Spring   Fold   Roll   Push/Pull   Hinge

PAYLOAD BAY

Create a model of
Webb that folds
to fit into this
dotted area

Activity 3.4: Pack Your Payload

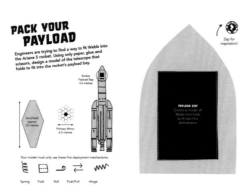

Background to this Activity

The James Webb Space Telescope is the most ambitious space telescope humans have built to date. Its primary mirror measures 6.5 meters in diameter and its kite-shaped sunshield is approximately 22 metres by 10 metres when deployed (similar to the size of a tennis court). If we tried to send a telescope this large into space without folding it up to make it smaller, we would need a rocket far bigger than any we have currently built.

To fit Webb into the Ariane 5 rocket – Webb's vehicle into space – engineers designed it to carefully fold up. But fitting Webb into the rocket wasn't their only challenge. Engineers had to ensure that the telescope could unfold (or deploy) properly in space.

For reference images of how Webb was designed to fit in the 'payload bay' of the Ariane 5 rocket (i.e. the part of a rocket which contains the payload – the item/s being sent to space), see the images on the Activity web page.

Most notably, you'll see that Webb's primary mirror is designed so that the rows of hexagonal mirrors on either side fold back at 90-degree angles, so that the mirror fits in the rocket. The sunshield membrane rolls up and its frame folds up on either side of the primary mirror for launch. The secondary mirror is held in place by a support structure made of three 'arms', one of which hinges over the primary mirror when Webb is inside the rocket. Webb's solar arrays hinged out during the early stages of deployment, to provide the telescope with power.

An excellent clip containing an overview the key components of Webb, along with how they folded up for launch, is available by visiting the Activity web page (see Useful Links). This clip also shows the telescope being built, giving a sense of its scale. NOTE: This clip shows an incorrect launch date of 2018.

Resources Required

- Tablet or device to access Zap code (optional — see Useful Links)
- Craft paper and other D&T materials
- Glue
- Scissors

Useful Links

Visit **discoverydiaries.org/ activities/pack-your-payload** to download Zappar app content to use offline (PowerPoints, videos and image bundles etc.) and to access links to other info, which may be useful in planning and running this lesson.

Running the Activity

On the Activity web page, you'll find a clip showing how Webb will unfold in space. Show students this clip and ask them if they notice something about the date in the clip. Have the students seen this launch on the news? (Go on to explain that the date has been pushed back.) Ask students the questions below in relation to the clip. This will help to encourage an understanding of the telescope and its mechanisms.

Explain to the students that this activity asks them to plan (through discussion and experimentation) and design a model of the telescope that will fold away and fit into the payload bay. The number of components students need to include can be adjusted, according to ability. As a minimum though, models should include:

- Solar panels
- Sunshield
- Primary mirror

More capable students can be encouraged to include:

- the antenna (referred to in the clip as the communication dishes)
- Secondary mirror

Explain to students that they will need to use the different methods listed on the worksheet to make the model so that it will deploy. Allow students time to experiment with these different methods, so they have an understanding of how folding, rolling and manipulating paper in different ways will help them create a model that can 'deploy'. Use pop-up picture books to demonstrate applications of these methods that students might already be familiar with.

Q/A: Discuss in small groups/tables:

- What ways can we make paper move?
- How can we make paper bounce/ spring up?
- How can you make the paper become smaller?

Discuss students' answers and share with the rest of the class. Make sure all five different mechanisms are recorded on the class whiteboard, so students can refer to these during their plan/making.

Divide the class into small mixed ability groups.

Provide each group with resources needed – paper, glue and scissors, etc.

Explain to students they will have some thinking and talking time to discuss their ideas. Give students time for individuals to discuss their ideas with the person next to them. Students will need to think about how they are going to create the telescope and what mechanisms they will use where.

*Got notes?
Write them
here!*

Allow time for students to share their ideas with their peers – this will help support and allow others to 'magpie ideas.' This will also allow students the opportunity to change or improve their ideas.

Ensure that all students understand the entire purpose of the task. At this point, you might want to provide them with additional information regarding examples of ways to carry out the task. Point out to students that they can use more than one of the deployment mechanisms to deploy each component of Webb (e.g. roll and hinge or fold for the sunshield).

Solutions to the Activity

In order for their telescope to deploy properly, students should create a model that unfolds in this order (suggested methods for each mechanism in brackets):

- Solar array (fold and hinge)
- Antenna (hinge)
- Sunshield (roll and hinge)
- Secondary mirror (hinge)
- Primary mirror (fold)

This means that they will have to fold it up in reverse order.

Questions for the Class

- Who built Webb?
- Why is it important that Webb folds away?
- How did they refer to the size of the heat insulation sunshield?
- How long will the journey take and how far will it travel?
- What did you notice about the way Webb unfolds?
- What mechanisms did you see in the clip?
- Why do the scientists have to wait for so long before they can use the telescope?

Additional Challenges / Extension Activities

Taking on the role of Telescope Engineer, students could explain the different mechanisms they have used in their model, by demonstrating their design solution either in person or by recording a presentation.

Students could be encouraged to research other telescopes and create a model.

Students could write a diary entry in the perspective of a person working for NASA, covering the lead-up the launch/the actual building of the telescope.

Record an interview: a Q&A session with an employee of NASA and the news team.

Challenge students to think of other ways to make a self-deploying structure.

Ideas for Differentiation

Support:

- For support, students could work in a guided group/with a partner.

- Students to be given ideas via prompt cards to help scaffold their learning if needed. These can include the different mechanisms.

- Students to create a planned drawing with mechanisms labelled on the plan. This will help to structure the learners and allow them to follow the plan.

Challenge:

- Students to be in mixed ability groupings.

- Students to work independent.

- Students to be given ideas prompt cards to help scaffold their learning if needed.

- Students can be given opportunity to draw a quick plan on a whiteboard to follow if needed.

Teacher Tip!

Allow students to watch the animated deployment sequence (see Links on the activity page) several times, to help them understand the various steps involved.

_____

_____

_____

_____

_____

_____

_____

_____

CHAPTER THREE WORD SEARCH

Zap for the answers!

Find the words you've learnt in this chapter and add them to your Visual Dictionary of Deep Space at the back of the book.
Words can go forward, backward and diagonally.

Y	J	P	A	M	O	V	M	O	T
M	R	I	A	W	Q	E	I	E	C
I	T	E	P	Y	T	T	R	K	U
R	J	L	V	H	L	U	I	O	R
R	R	N	O	O	T	O	K	P	T
O	A	D	Q	C	C	E	A	Y	S
R	B	I	U	L	M	S	Z	D	N
S	C	R	A	N	U	B	I	D	O
V	T	R	L	G	U	D	B	D	C
S	E	N	G	I	N	E	E	R	P
T	N	E	M	I	R	E	P	X	E

Target = 8 words beginning with:

C E P D M S E M

Chapter Three: Word Search

Solutions to this Activity

Background to this Activity

Word searches are a fun way to build your students' vocabularies. You can extend these activities with the Visual Dictionary of Deep Space (see below).

Running the Activity

The word searches provide an opportunity to review and discuss what has been covered in each chapter. For each word search, look at the starting letters noted below the word search grid. As a class or in student pairs, discuss what some of the words might be. Ask students if they can identify any of those words.

As students complete the word searches, remind them to write new words in their Visual Dictionary of Deep Space (see Activity 6.2: discoverydiaries.org/activities/visual-dictionary-of-deep-space/).

Word Search Chapter 3: Discovery, Construct, Experiment, Structure, Mirror, Method, Engineer, Payload

Definitions:

Construct: to make or build

Engineer: a person who designs, builds, maintains or controls things (e.g. structures, machinery) and/or systems (e.g/ software, electrics)

Resources Required

- Rulers
- Computers, devices or textbooks for research
- Pens/Pencils
- Visual Dictionary of Deep Space
- Tablet or device to access Zap code (optional — see Useful Links)

Useful Links

Visit **discoverydiaries.org/activities/chapter-three-word-search** to download Zappar app content to use offline (PowerPoints, videos and image bundles etc.) and to access links to other info, which may be useful in planning and running this lesson.

Payload: the items to be transported in a vehicle, including rockets that are sent to space

Discovery: the action or process of discovering; the process of finding information, especially for the first time

Mirror: a surface, typically glass-coated with a metal amalgam, which reflects an image

Structure: a building or object made from several parts; the arrangement of different parts or elements of something complex

Experiment: a scientific procedure undertaken to make a discovery, test a hypothesis or demonstrate a known fact

Method: a procedure for accomplishing something

Ideas for Differentiation

Support:

- Work as a class or in groups to find definitions, assigning words to students.

- Work as a class or in groups to create a song using vocabulary from the chapter.

- Provide hidden words to students.

Challenge:

- Once students have completed the word searches, ask them to develop their own. Download and print our blank word search template to use with your class (see Useful Links). They can then test a classmate with their word search. Differentiate by giving clues as the whole word, the first letter or a definition of the word.

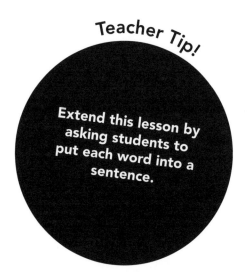

Teacher Tip!

Extend this lesson by asking students to put each word into a sentence.

Got notes? Write them here!

_____
_____
_____
_____
_____
_____
_____
_____

CHAPTER 4:
JOURNEY TO DEEP SPACE

Now that students have packed their telescopes into
their rockets, it's time to launch! While learning about
Webb's journey to space and its complex deployment
sequence, students will practice their coding and
decoding skills, before exploring the far reaches
of space.

What's inside this chapter?

4.1 – Parking Skills
Create a precise set of commands to guide Webb to its orbital position
in deep space.
> Science + Coding

4.2 – Deep Space Decoder
Decode Webb's encrypted deployment sequence, then put the steps
in the correct order.
> Science + Coding

4.3 – Calibrate for Discovery
To calibrate Webb, measure the angles to different points of interest
in space.
> Science + Maths

4.4 – Chapter Four Word Search
Find eight scientific words from Chapter Four.
> Science + Literacy

PARKING SKILLS!

Congratulations! Your telescope is ready to launch! But where will you park it? Compare the four different options, then follow the maze to find the best spot. Once you have the path, program the commands below so Webb knows where to go!

Zap for answers →

Manchester city centre
1

A desert mountain top
2

Just above Earth's atmosphere
3

A cold, dark place in space, four times further than our Moon
4

<Top Secret Commands>

Move	Direction ✳	Distance (cm)
1	←	1
2	↗	1
3		
4		
5		
6		
7		
8		
9		
10		

Activity 4.1: Parking Skills

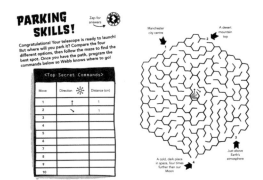

Background to this Activity

The James Webb Space Telescope studies our Universe from a position in space called L2 (or second Lagrangian point), which is almost four times further away from Earth than the Moon or 1.5 million kilometres from Earth. By comparison, the Hubble Space Telescope orbits Earth at a distance of 568 kilometres.

This activity provides students with the opportunity to consider why we go to the effort and expense of sending telescopes to space, rather than just studying our Universe from Earth. If we attempted to study the Universe from a populated area – such as Manchester's city centre – the city lights and weather would create light pollution, reducing visibility even with a powerful telescope. It'd be even more difficult to study space from a city centre with high air pollution or smog.

Observing would improve from a desert mountain top. There is less chance of rain and cloud and our telescope would be above more of the atmosphere. To understand the advantages of being somewhere high, imagine looking across a parking lot on a hot day. Objects appear shimmery and hazy because light bounces and bends as it travels through turbulent hot air. The same thing happens when we look through the Earth's atmosphere at objects in space. This is why stars twinkle! Observing from a high place means we look through less atmosphere and therefore get clearer and more stable views.

Although there are many large, powerful telescopes on Earth, they can't observe all the different types of light given off by things in space. Our atmosphere is transparent to the optical light our eyes can detect and to some radio waves, but it is (thankfully!) opaque to other types of light such as ultraviolet (UV), X-rays, and gamma rays. The atmosphere also blocks the infrared light that Webb is designed to detect, and which is necessary to study extremely distant things in space and things in very dusty environments, like newly formed stars and planets. Infrared telescopes like Webb – along with those studying other types of light blocked by the atmosphere – must be in space to work.

Resources Required

- Tablet or device to access Zap code (optional — see Useful Links)

Useful Links

Visit **discoverydiaries.org/ activities/parking-skills** to download Zappar app content to use offline (PowerPoints, videos and image bundles etc.) and to access links to other info, which may be useful in planning and running this lesson.

Why can't Webb be positioned closer to Earth, like the Hubble Space Telescope? In order to study infrared light from things in the Universe, Webb must be in a cold, stable place where it can see the whole of the sky over time. In addition, Webb's sunshield must be able to protect its mirrors and instruments from the heat of the Sun, Earth and Moon to maintain the required low temperature on the 'cold side' (see Activity 3.1: Blueprint for Space for information about Webb's hot and cold sides). An orbital position called "L2" – which is on the opposite side of the Earth from the Sun and almost four times further away from Earth than our Moon – meets both of these requirements. L2 is about 1.5 million kilometres from Earth.

But sending a telescope so far into space has some disadvantages. Webb is too far away from Earth to be maintained or repaired, should it break or be damaged. Hubble was serviced by astronauts five times. During these services, instruments were replaced due to failure or wear, and other instruments were added when newer technology became available. These repair missions were possible because of Hubble's proximity to Earth.

Running the Activity

Explain to students that this activity will involve thinking about the position of the telescope. Show students where L2 is using an image of Webb's orbital position which you can find on the Activity's web page (see Useful Links). Discuss the pros and cons of the suggested sites, using the background information above. Ask students to make their own list, or contribute to a whole class list. e.g:

Manchester City Centre

Pros:

- Any problems could be fixed on site
- Information would be readily available

Cons:

- Light and pollution would decrease the effectiveness of the telescope
- City centres are crowded and there is little space for a telescope

A cold, dark place in space, 4x further away than the moon

Pros:

- Infrared light from a distant star has not been absorbed by Earth's atmosphere
- The whole sky can be viewed over time from L2

Cons:

- Expensive and technically difficult to launch a telescope into space
- Any malfunctions are too far away to fix

Got notes? Write them here!

Ask students to suggest why, based on their lists, we go to the effort and expense of sending the telescope to space.

Ask students to start by completing the maze on the worksheet. Next, show students how to identify and record the commands on the grid to guide the telescope to its destination.

(Depending on the age and ability of the class, identify the best of the four locations.)

Solutions to the Activity

<Top Secret Commands>		
Move	Direction ❄	Distance (cm)
1	↑	1
2	↘	1
3	↓	1
4	↗	1
5	↓	4
6	↙	3
7	↖	1
8	↓	1
9	↘	1
10	↓	3

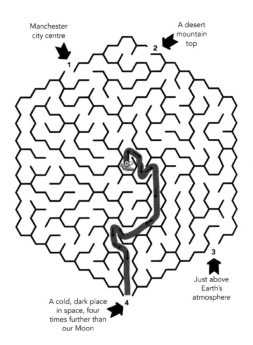

Manchester city centre

A desert mountain top

Just above Earth's atmosphere

A cold, dark place in space, four times further than our Moon

Questions for the Class

- Why do we send telescopes to space?
- Why is the positioning of Webb so important?
- What are the difficulties of having the telescope so far away?
- How can the telescope communicate with Earth?
- Why do we use set commands to program machines?

Additional Challenges / Extension Activities

Ask students to use squared paper to design their own map/maze with missing directions.

Investigate the locations of different telescopes on Earth and in space and think about their similarities and differences.

If possible, arrange a visit to a telescope/observatory (see Useful Links for locations). Think about why that site was chosen.

Ideas for Differentiation

Support:

- Provide students with pros and cons cards to match with a particular site

- Discuss as a class which would be the best

- Have students work with a partner to write the sequence of commands

- Provide some initial commands to model the activity for students to follow

Challenge:

- Allow students to decide which location they need to travel to (1, 2, 3 or 4) prior to completing the maze

- Create a reverse series of instructions to describe an imaginary return journey

Teacher Tip!

During an ICT class, ask students to create their own mazes using free maze generating software. They can then challenge classmates to solve the maze and use the commands to program their telescope.

DEEP SPACE DECODER

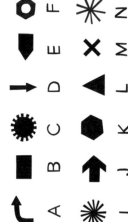

Hi space explorer,

I'm Vincent Geers, a software engineer at the UK Astronomy Technology Centre. It's time to deploy your telescope. I have sent you ar encrypted message containing the deployment sequence. It is critical your telescope follows this sequence exactly. Decode the sequence, put them in the correct order, then destroy this top secret message.

<Deployment Sequence>

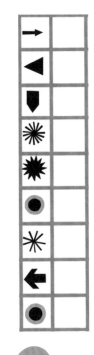
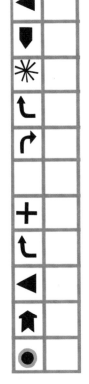

Zap to watch the deployment video and put the sequence into the right order

2

<Encryption code>

A · B · C · D · E · F · G · H · I · J · K · L · M · N · O · P · Q · R · S · T · U · V · W · X · Y · Z

Activity 4.2: Deep Space Decoder

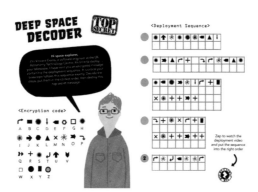

A 12-minute animation that shows Webb's launch, deployment sequence and orbital position, can be found on the Activity's web page (see Useful Links). It is quite detailed and includes complex scientific vocabulary.

A shorter (5-minute) version of the animation showing the deployment sequence is also available on the Activity's web page.

Background to this Activity

This activity uses the James Webb Space Telescope's deployment sequence as the basis for developing visual literacy and coding skills. Prepare students by first completing Activity 3.1: Blueprint for Space – so they are familiar with Webb's different components – and Activity 3.4: Pack Your Payload so they understand that Webb is folded up when it is launched into space.

The journey from Earth to L2 – where Webb is positioned to study our Universe – takes 30 days. During this journey, Webb's components deploy in a complex sequence. For the purposes of this activity, deployment has been simplified, focusing on some of the key components of Webb. This will help students understand that the way Webb folds up to fit into its rocket relates not only to how it deploys but also to the functions of its various parts.

These animations show how complex the deployment of a space telescope is. Each step of deployment must be carefully planned and calculated before launch, and the deployment sequence pre-programmed. Coding must be error-free and clearly expressed, otherwise the telescope won't deploy correctly, resulting in potential damage or mission failure.

Running the Activity

In this activity the students will crack a coded message to activate the deployment of Webb. Start by revising the telescope's purpose and the parts that the students have learnt from previous activities.

Explain to the students that Webb is packaged carefully before it is launched into space. Ask the students if they can suggest any reasons why. Establish that it is because of Webb's huge size and also to keep it protected and make it less likely

Resources Required

- Tablet or device to access Zap code (optional — see Useful Links)

Useful Links

Visit **discoverydiaries.org/activities/ deep-space-decoder** to download Zappar app content to use offline (PowerPoints, videos and image bundles etc.) and to access links to other info, which may be useful in planning and running this lesson.

to be damaged as it travels through space. Watch an animation showing the deployment sequence by visiting the Activity's web page (see Useful Links).

Discuss the sequence step by step. Ask the students to suggest why the parts deploy in a certain order. For example, can the students explain why the sunshield or the solar panels deploy early in the process? Use dictionaries to check the meanings of words.

Introduce the activity and model how to solve the coded elements. Once students have decoded each component, they can order them according to Webb's deployment sequence.

Solutions to the Activity

3: Sunshield — Webb's sunshield protects its instruments from the heat and light from the Sun, Earth and Moon. Its complex design means it takes three days to fully deploy, starting on Day 3 after launch. First, the pallet on either side of Webb is released, then the sunshield – made up of five layers of a reflective and heat-resistant material called Kapton – is released. The sunshield is then stretched out and tensioned, to create gaps between each of its layers to deflect heat away from Webb's instruments.

1: Solar Panels — Thirty minutes after launch, Webb's solar panels are deployed to provide it with power. Webb only has a small battery so it relies on its solar panels for power.

4: Secondary Mirror — On Day 11 of Webb's journey to L2, its secondary mirror is unhinged to sit in front of the primary mirror. The secondary mirror focuses the light collected by the primary mirror and directs it into Webb's instruments.

5: Primary Mirror — The final stage of Webb's deployment is the primary mirror. In order for the huge primary mirror to fit inside the payload dock, its outer panels are folded back at 90-degree angles. From Day 12-14 after launch, these 'wings' are deployed in turn.

2: Antenna — Two hours after launch, Webb's antenna is released but it is not deployed until one day after launch. The antenna provides two-way communication between Webb and Earth, receiving commands and sending its findings to NASA's Deep Space Network.

Questions for the Class

- Why does the telescope follow a particular deployment sequence?

- Why does a deployment sequence need to be carefully coded before a telescope is launched into space?

- What problems might the telescope encounter as it travels into space?

Got notes? Write them here!

- What is the difference between coding and encryption?
- Why do we use encryption? What are some examples of encryption that we use on Earth?

Additional Challenges / Extension Activities

Link to English and write an explanation text about the process of Webb's deployment. Include time and causal conjunctions.

Research how a telescope works.

Investigate how solar panels convert light into electricity.

Explore the history of encoding messages and develop your own code to send top secret messages.

Ideas for Differentiation

Support:

- Work collaboratively on the code or add in some letters before the students start.
- Provide some of the words and ask the students to identify which encoded word they are.

Challenge:

- Write your own coded message for an aspect of the telescope's deployment.
- Create codes for deployment steps which are not in the worksheet and add these to the sequence.

Teacher Tip!

Extend this activity by asking students to create a code for any other steps in Webb's deployment sequence, or by writing coded messages for classmates to decode.

CALIBRATE FOR DISCOVERY

Get your protractor ready, space explorer. Measure the angles to point Webb towards new discoveries.

90°

Reference Line

0°

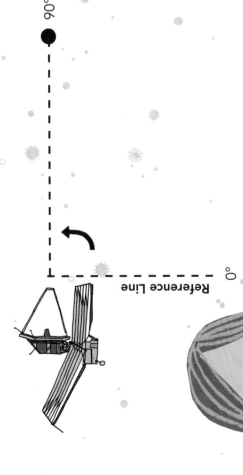

Hi space explorer,

I'm Pamela Klaassen, an instrument scientist working on Webb. I have identified five points of interest that I'd like you to investigate. Calibrate the telescope by measuring the angles to each spot.

1. Neptune
Estimated:
Exact:
Angle Type:

2. Hubble Deep Field
Estimated:
Exact:
Angle Type:

3. Trappist-1
Estimated:
Exact:
Angle Type:

4. Pinwheel Galaxy
Estimated:
Exact:
Angle Type:

5. Pillars of Creation
Estimated:
Exact:
Angle Type:

Zap to discover more about these points of interest

Activity 4.3: Calibrate for Discovery

Background to this Activity

The James Webb Space Telescope will study our Universe from deep space for at least five years. During this time, different researchers will use it to study specific space objects and answer scientific questions about our Universe. Scientists who want to use Webb must pitch research proposals. A peer review committee decides who gets to use the telescope, after reviewing the proposals.

In just five months, 13 different research groups will use Webb to conduct surveys of galaxies, observe the formation of stars, examine the chemistry of stars and study exoplanets. These 13 research groups represent over 250 investigators from 18 countries and 106 institutions, demonstrating that Webb is a global project with a local story.

In this activity, students are asked to take on the role of scientific investigators, 'calibrating' Webb so that it can then look at objects of interest.

Running the Activity

Before completing the worksheet, ensure students know how to use a protractor (or angle measurer) to measure angles:

Place the protractor along the reference line, with the midpoint on the vertex of the angle.

Ensure that the 0 degrees line of the protractor is in line with the reference line.

Following the direction of the arrow, read the degrees where the line to the point of interest crosses the number scale.

Introduce the concept of calibration. (Calibration refers to the act of evaluating and adjusting the precision and accuracy of measurement equipment.)

Point out the vertical reference line on the worksheet and demonstrate measuring the angle from Webb's secondary mirror to the example, which has been marked on the worksheet as 90°. Model how to estimate, considering the angle types (acute, right, obtuse). Then demonstrate how to measure the angle accurately, arriving at the answer: 90 degrees.

Resources Required

- Tablet or device to access Zap code (optional — see Useful Links)
- Protractors
- Rulers

Useful Links

Visit **discoverydiaries.org/activities/ calibrate-for-discovery** to download Zappar app content to use offline (PowerPoints, videos and image bundles etc.) and to access links to other info, which may be useful in planning and running this lesson.

Now ask the class to work alongside you as you look at the next point of interest, Neptune. Note that the angle is not drawn, so model using a ruler to draw an accurate line from Webb's secondary mirror (see Activity 3.3: Blueprint for Space if you aren't familiar with Webb's structure) to the centre of the circle marking Neptune.

Discuss the type of angle and use this to help make an estimate. Allow time for students to make their own estimate. Ensure students understand that an estimate is an approximated measurement.

Model how to align the protractor to the reference line and the vertex of the angle, ensuring that the crosshairs are correctly placed. Allow time for students to measure the angle and record. Have a student demonstrate measuring the angle to the class. Check that students have used the correct scale when reading the protractor. Students should then be able to identify the type of angle.

Students should now be able to repeat these steps independently, for the remaining angles. Students could use different coloured pens or pencils to make the angles clearer.

Encourage students to check measurements with a partner as they progress.

Complete the activity by sharing the solutions with the students.

Solutions to the Activity

Students in Lower KS2 would be expected to be accurate to within 2 degrees.

Students in Upper KS2 would be expected to be accurate to within 1 degree.

Note that there may be some variation in results, depending on how accurately students draw lines from the secondary mirror to the centre of each point of interest.

1: Neptune

Exact: 117°
Angle Type: Obtuse
(Acceptable range: 116-119°)

2: Hubble Deep Field

Exact: 77°
Angle Type: Acute
(Acceptable range: 76-79°)

3: Trappist-1

Exact: 58°
Angle Type: Acute
(Acceptable range: 56-59°)

4: Pinwheel Galaxy

Exact: 100°
Angle Type: Obtuse
(Acceptable range: 98-101°)

5: Pillars of Creation

Exact: 82°
Angle Type: Acute
(Acceptable range: 80-83°)

Got notes? Write them here!

Questions for the Class

- What does calibration mean?

- Why is the calibration of the telescope so important?

- Which angle is the largest? By how many degrees is it larger than a right angle?

- Add two more angles to ensure that the calibration is as accurate as possible. What types of angles are these and what do they measure?

- Can you draw an angle of 200°? What type of angle is this?

Additional Challenges / Extension Activities

Write a research proposal pitch, arguing why it's important to study a particular space object (real or imaginary – based on the points of interest) and what you hope to learn through your research.

Ideas for Differentiation

Support:

- Draw and mark in the angles before giving the students the sheet. Ask them to name each angle and estimate its size.

- Some students may benefit from working in a guided group, working through the estimate and naming process for each angle with an adult to support.

- Provide students with the key vocabulary they will need e.g. acute, obtuse, right angle.

- Students could be provided with a range of angle measurements to select the correct measurements from.

- Lower Key Stage 2 may name and estimate the angles but not measure unless appropriate.

Challenge:

- Measure the angles to the exact degree.

- Students working at greater depth within age related expectations could be asked to mark in different angles including acute, obtuse and reflex.

Teacher Tip!

Extend this activity by dividing the class into five and allocated a point of interest to each group. Groups can then research their point of interest and present their findings.

CHAPTER FOUR
WORD SEARCH

Zap for the answers!

Find the words you've learnt in this chapter and add them to your Visual Dictionary of Deep Space at the back of the book.
Words can go forward, backward and diagonally.

N	C	A	L	I	B	R	A	T	E
A	O	V	G	T	I	D	Y	N	S
C	R	I	H	V	E	B	C	E	E
E	O	U	T	P	B	T	M	M	Q
K	W	M	L	P	Q	X	M	U	U
X	H	O	M	S	Y	A	V	R	E
W	Y	H	L	A	R	R	U	T	N
Q	I	S	K	G	N	D	C	S	C
E	E	D	O	C	E	D	K	N	E
T	W	R	V	X	Z	G	S	I	E
T	P	F	C	A	G	R	D	A	H

Target = 8 words beginning with:

C D P C E S D I

Chapter Four: Word Search

Solutions to this Activity

Background to this Activity

Word searches are a fun way to build your students' vocabularies. You can extend these activities with the Visual Dictionary of Deep Space (see below).

Running the Activity

The word searches provide an opportunity to review and discuss what has been covered in each chapter. For each word search, look at the starting letters noted below the word search grid. As a class or in student pairs, discuss what some of the words might be. Ask students if they can identify any of those words.

As students complete the word searches, remind them to write new words in their Visual Dictionary of Deep Space (see Activity 6.2).

Word Search Chapter 4: Commands, Deploy, Program, Calibrate, Encryption, Sequence, Decode, Instrument

Definitions:

Commands: a set of specific orders or instructions designed to achieve a particular outcome

Resources Required

- Rulers
- Computers, devices or textbooks for research
- Pens/Pencils
- Visual Dictionary of Deep Space
- Tablet or device to access Zap code (optional — see Useful Links)

Useful Links

Visit **discoverydiaries.org/ activities/chapter-four-word-search** to download Zappar app content to use offline (PowerPoints, videos and image bundles etc.) and to access links to other info, which may be useful in planning and running this lesson.

Deploy: bring into effective action; to make something ready for use

Program: a set of related activities with a particular long-term goal; to provide (a computer or other machine) with coded instructions for the automatic performance of a task

Calibrate: to correlate the readers (of an instrument) with those of a standard, in order to check the instrument's accuracy

Encryption: the process of converting information or data into a code, especially to prevent unauthorised access

Sequence: a particular order in which related things follow each other; to arrange in a particular order

Decode: to convert a coded message into intelligible language

Instrument: a tool or implement, especially one for precise work

Ideas for Differentiation

Support:

- Work as a class or in groups to find definitions, assigning words to students.
- Work as a class or in groups to create a song using vocabulary from the chapter.
- Provide hidden words to students.

Challenge:

- Once students have completed the word searches, ask them to develop their own. Download and print our blank word search template to use with your class (see Useful Links). They can then test a classmate with their word search. Differentiate by giving clues as the whole word, the first letter or a definition of the word.

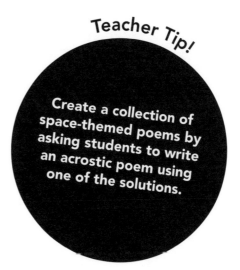

Teacher Tip!

Create a collection of space-themed poems by asking students to write an acrostic poem using one of the solutions.

Got notes? Write them here!

CHAPTER 5: GROUNDBREAKING DISCOVERIES

Visual literacy and analysis are important skills for every scientist. Now that their telescopes are safely in orbit, students can gather data, analyse it to draw conclusions and then report their findings to other space experts.

What's inside this chapter?

5.1 – First Findings
Analyse and compare an optical and an infrared image, to identify new astronomical discoveries.
> Science + Art

5.2 – Data Detective
Use the information in Dataset 1 to identify which planet in Dataset 2 might support human life.
> Science + Coding

5.3 – Visualising the Universe
Create a scientific poster that includes diagrams, graphs and images to present scientific findings.
> Science + Art

5.4 – Chapter Five Word Search
Find eight scientific words from Chapter Five.
> Science + Literacy

FIRST FINDINGS

Congratulations, your telescope has sent back its first infrared image and – WOW! – we can see so many things that optical images haven't captured. Help us analyse this image…

Hi space observer!

I'm Alastair Bruce, an astronomer at the Royal Observatory, Edinburgh. Help me understand more about your infrared image. What differences can you spot between it and the optical image? Colour the differences you see. Can you name any of the celestial wonders your image reveals?

Zap to explore the infrared Universe!

Optical

Infrared

Activity 5.1: First Findings

Background to this Activity

The James Webb Space Telescope uses infrared technology to observe space. This means it can see through the space dust that has previously obscured our view and prevented us from learning more about how stars are formed inside dark dust clouds. Its huge primary mirror also means it can collect light from galaxies that formed about 400 million years after the Big Bang. Because they're so far away, light waves from these galaxies have been stretched to longer, infrared wavelengths as they cross our expanding Universe. No other space telescope has been sensitive enough to detect these very faint galaxies in the infrared light needed to see them. Using Webb, we can see further and in greater detail than ever before.

Running the Activity

Consider enlarging the worksheet onto A3 paper for class discussion of this activity.

Talk about how the two images are similar/different and discuss reasons for this. Relate this to prior learning about optical photographs versus infrared images (see Activity 2.4: Infrared Selfie) and the evolution of telescope technology (see Activity 1.4: The Starry Messengers).

Students should use two pieces of tracing paper to mark out visible features, first from the optical image and then, with the other piece of tracing paper, from the infrared image. By overlaying the two, they will be able to make comparisons more easily. They can also use different colours to highlight differences between the two images.

Students can use the Zap code to access information about the different celestial features, or they can refer to the PowerPoint presentation accompanying this activity.

In tracing the visible features, students will have created their own 'distant galaxy' pictures based on the images provided. This lesson leads naturally on to further discussion about artistic representations of galaxies. In 1850, astronomer Lord Rosse depicted for the first time what a distant galaxy might look like, in a drawing called 'Whirlpool Galaxy'. You can view his drawing by visiting the Activity's web page — see Useful Links.

Resources Required

- Tablet or device to access Zap code (optional — see Useful Links)
- Tracing paper (optional)
- Paints and art supplied (optional)

Useful Links

Visit **discoverydiaries.org/ activities/first-findings** to download Zappar app content to use offline (PowerPoints, videos and image bundles etc.) and to access links to other info, which may be useful in planning and running this lesson.

Many of us will be familiar with Vincent van Gogh's 'Starry Night' painting (1889), which is commonly thought to depict the night sky. In 2015, US artist and photographer Michael Benson suggested in his book *Cosmigraphics* (Abrams, 2014) that the painting actually depicts galaxies in the universe, and was likely inspired by drawings of the cosmos at the time. There is further information on this theory on the Activity's web page — see Useful Links.

Encourage students to discuss how van Gogh's painting 'Starry Night' may have been influenced by the artistic representation of the Whirlpool Galaxy. Discuss the use of texture, movement, swirls and patterns as well as colour to add depth and tone. On the Activity web page there is an animation of the painting which enhances the movement within the paint strokes.

Using a selection of paints, students could experiment with a range of techniques to create their own artistic interpretations of the distant galaxies and other celestial features captured by Webb. Students could create their own comparisons of the night sky as viewed with an optical telescope or an infrared telescope like Webb.

A class display could show students' work beside the telescope images.

Solutions to the Activity

M81: Messier 81 is an example of a spiral galaxy. When viewed in infrared, we can see star-forming regions. We can also see the spiral arm structure more clearly, revealing areas of dust and gas that are ready to become new stars.

The Sombrero Galaxy: This galaxy has a distinct ring of dust that circles a bulge of stars. When viewed in infrared, we can clearly see its dust and inner flat disk. Because we view this galaxy from its side, it appears very flat. Our Milky Way would look like this if it was view from the side too.

Maffei 2: This barred starburst galaxy is very difficult for us to see without infrared because thick clouds in our galaxy obscure it. With infrared we can see the shape of Maffei 2.

L1014: This dark cloud hides a secret that we can only see in infrared: a protostar – or baby star! With infrared technology, we can see a disk of gas surrounding the protostar. This feeds it and provides material for building planets.

NGC 253: When we view this galaxy with just visible light, its shape is difficult to determine because of our viewing angle, its dark dust clouds and the light from its massive stars. Infrared reveals the long spiral arms and the central bar, showing that NGC 253 is a barred galaxy.

Got notes? Write them here!

Pillars of Creation: Part of a young cluster of stars in the Eagle Nebula, the Pillars of Creation are composed of gas and dust, which prevents us from discovering what's within them with visible light. With infrared light however, we're able to see a multitude of stars which are otherwise hidden.

A 'surprise' distant galaxy: Because Webb's mirror is so huge and its instruments detect infrared light, it can catch light from galaxies that are so distant, we otherwise wouldn't know they're there. What would you name a galaxy if you were to discover one?

Find videos and illustrations of each solution on the activity web page — see Useful Links.

Questions for the Class

- How are the two images similar?
- What differences can you see between the two images?
- Why is the optical image different to the infrared image?
- Do you think van Gogh's painting was based on what we can see of our night sky or was he creating a painting based on a telescope image? Why/why not?

Additional Challenges / Extension Activities

Students could look at other artists' depictions of galaxies/nebulas, etc. Check out Alexander Calder's work or, for more contemporary examples, work by Katie Paterson.

Students could experiment with other media such as watercolour paints, to create additional paintings of the celestial features.

More able students could use ICT software such as drawing applications to create an image with labelled celestial features.

Ideas for Differentiation

Support:

- Students can work in pairs to compare and contrast the two images.
- Provide adult support with navigating the web resources, such as the PowerPoint presentation.

Challenge:

- Peer assessment of completed paintings.
- Students could be given responsibilities in creating the class display by creating labels, headings and short pieces of text to accompany the images.

Teacher Tip!

Inspire students and support their understanding of why infrared is so useful to astronomers by showing them the 'Infrared Universe' videos in Links on the activity's page.

DATA DETECTIVE

Dataset 1: Detected Gases

Gas	Clues	Characteristics
carbon dioxide		
water vapour		
carbon monoxide		
methane		

Dataset 2: Atmospheric Data from 10 Exoplanets

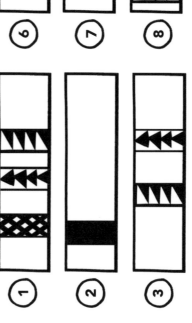
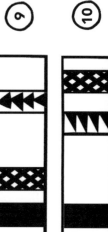

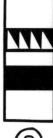

1 2 3 4 5 6 7 8 9 10

Hi space explorer! I'm Beth Biller and I study exoplanets! Your super-sensitive infrared telescope can see light through the atmospheres of exoplanets, and even detect patterns that can tell us what that air is made of. I see you have already collected data for 10 recently-observed planets. Can you work out if any of these might support life?

Zap to learn more about exoplanets

Look at the clues in Dataset 1. What are the emojis telling us about these gases? Can you find out more about them?

One of the carbons is made up of **carbon + 1 oxygen** and the other is **carbon + 2 oxygen**. Which is which? (Pssst. There's a clue in the name!)

Analyse Dataset 2 and colour-code the planets into these categories:

● Definitely no life here!
● Unlikely to support life
● Planet most likely to support life

Activity 5.2: Data Detective

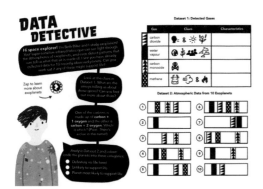

Background to this Activity

The James Webb Space Telescope plays a key role in helping us learn about the atmospheres of planets – even those in other solar systems (known as exoplanets). By analysing data collected by Webb, scientists can discover which chemicals are present in a planet's atmosphere. This means they can search for the building blocks of life – like water, carbon dioxide and methane – elsewhere in the Universe.

But how do scientists do this? One method involves studying a distant planet as it passes between us and its sun (a star). When a planet passes (or 'transits') in front of a star, a fraction of starlight is absorbed by the planet's atmosphere. Using spectroscopy – measuring the intensity of light at different wavelengths – scientists can determine which wavelengths have been absorbed. Different chemical elements and compounds absorb light at specific wavelengths, forming 'chemical fingerprints' which can be used to work out which gases are in exoplanet atmospheres.

This complex concept is explained clearly and simply in an animation found on the Activity web page (see Useful Links), and will help students understand the premise of this activity.

Teachers wishing to simplify the theory behind this activity can explain to students that Webb's scientific instruments are used to identify the gases in an exoplanet's atmosphere.

Running the Activity

Hook:

What are exoplanets? What is needed on a planet to support life, and what might be signs of life? Why might we want to know about other habitable planets? Have an open discussion and question time with the class about this, uncovering prior understanding before going into more detail about the activity. Relate discussion back to Webb and its role in learning about exoplanets.

Starter:

Read through the activity and questions with the class. Model Dataset 1, asking the class what we know about these gases, and what we can interpret from the symbols.

Resources Required

- Tablet or device to access Zap code (optional — see Useful Links)

- Science Encyclopedia, Science Dictionaries or access to internet – to support research into the four gases: water, carbon dioxide, carbon monoxide, methane.

Useful Links

Visit **discoverydiaries.org/ activities/data-detective** to download Zappar app content to use offline (PowerPoints, videos and image bundles etc.) and to access links to other info, which may be useful in planning and running this lesson.

Some facts about each gas you might like to cover include:

Carbon dioxide:

- molecules are made of one carbon atom and two oxygen atoms

- is essential for animal and plant life on Earth. Green plants use carbon dioxide during photosynthesis, producing oxygen for humans and animals to breathe

- humans exhale carbon dioxide, which green plants can then use

- the fizz in fizzy drinks comes from dissolved carbon dioxide

Water:

- molecules are made of two hydrogen atoms and one oxygen atom

- is essential for life on Earth

- regulates human body temperature, carries nutrients and oxygen to cells, protects our organs and tissues and removes waste products

- 75% of the human brain and 50% of a living tree is water

Carbon monoxide:

- molecules are made from one carbon and one oxygen atom

- is a colourless, odorless gas

- is toxic to humans and animals who breathe oxygen

- comes from car emissions

Methane:

- molecules are made from one carbon atom and four hydrogen atoms

- is produced by living creatures, including cows and microbes

- is often used as fuel in the form of natural gas

- as a refined liquid, it can be used to fuel a rocket

Classify each gas as one of the following:

- toxic to life

- useful for life

- required for life

Students can create their own colour-coding system for these three options and colour in the circles on the worksheet accordingly.

Main Activity:

Using the information from Dataset 1, ask students to analyse each of the ten exoplanet 'fingerprints' in Dataset 2 and consider:

Which gases does it contain?

Does this planet contain anything toxic/useful/required?

For each data set, students need to discuss, reason and justify whether it is likely that life could exist on the planet, giving reasons for their answers. They can then colour-code that fingerprint accordingly.

Got notes? Write them here!

Plenary:

Can students present back, communicating which exoplanet they think is most likely to support life and their reasons why?

Solutions to the Activity

Dataset 1:

Carbon dioxide (one carbon + two oxygen) – released by animals and humans when they exhale; used by plants in photosynthesis

Water – essential for life

Carbon monoxide (one carbon + one oxygen) – a poisonous gas

Methane – a greenhouse gas produced by some rocks and lifeforms, used as a fuel

Dataset 2:

Definitely no life here: 1, 3, 4, 6, 8, 9

Unlikely to support life: 2, 7, 10

Exoplanet most likely to support life: 5

Questions for the Class

- What is an exoplanet?
- Why are we interested in exoplanets?
- Which exoplanet in the activity is most likely to support life and why?
- Which exoplanets in the activity cannot support life and why?

Additional Challenges / Extension Activities

For a simple challenge, students can research the four gases, giving reasons for how each affects life.

Can students, individually or in groups, research an exoplanet? How was it located? Which telescope found it? Where is it located? Is it likely to support life? Why? See Useful Links for resources to support this activity.

Ideas for Differentiation

Support:

- Give students fact files for water, carbon dioxide and carbon monoxide, to support their initial research.

Challenge:

- Allow independent research.
- Justify each exoplanet's likely to support life, with reasons. Can students use scientific evidence to justify their answers?

Teacher Tip!

Using Dataset 1, ask students to create atmospheric data for their own imagined exoplanets. They can then challenge their classmates to discover which exoplanets might be habitable.

VISUALISING THE UNIVERSE

Scientists are keen to hear about your discoveries. Use graphs, diagrams, drawings, photos or infographics to create a poster presentation on your findings.

Hi space scientist!
I'm Naomi Rowe-Gurney and I study giant planets. I hear you've made some interesting discoveries and observations with your discoveries and observations with your telescope. Create a visual poster that shows fellow researchers like me what you have discovered and the potential this has to change what we know about the Universe.

Zap for inspiration!

Activity 5.3: Visualising the Universe

Background to this Activity

Representing scientific findings and data visually is one way to quickly and effectively communicate and is therefore an important scientific skill. While we often encounter visual representations of data in everyday life, like graphs about our household energy usage or charts about the weather, scientists have a special way of sharing data visually in what's called an academic poster.

The purpose of an academic poster is to summarise the key information arising from research. It should be clear and attractive, so that it generates interest and encourages discussion. It is often used to support a talk or presentation but should also stand alone without verbal explanation, if it is displayed.

The most successful posters:

- have a short, compelling title

- have a total word count of 300-800 words

- use headings, bullet points and numbered lists to make it easy to read and follow

- use colour graphs, charts, infographics and other visual representations of data to communicate

- have a clean and consistent design and layout.

This activity challenges students to create an academic poster, using findings from work they've already completed in their Deep Space Diary. This may include information about new galaxies identified by Webb's infrared cameras (see Activity 5.1: First Findings), new planets and their atmospheres (see Activity 5.2: Data Detective) or even information about the James Webb Space Telescope itself.

Running the Activity

This is a largely open-ended task which will fit in well with various areas of focus within the Space topic. Prior to planning their own posters, students should be given lots of

Resources Required

- Tablet or device to access Zap code (optional — see Useful Links)

- Resources for poster creation

- Reference materials for research

- Desktop publishing tools (optional)

Useful Links

Visit **discoverydiaries.org/ activities/visualising-the-universe** to download Zappar app content to use offline (PowerPoints, videos and image bundles etc.) and to access links to other info, which may be useful in planning and running this lesson.

time to study examples of scientific posters, noting particular features which set them apart from other types of expository writing. This task would fit nicely into a unit of work on expository writing.

Exposure to the Genre

Remember that students are unlikely to have significant experience of scientific posters, but will be very familiar with posters more generally (e.g. adverts, signage, etc). Relate this task to prior learning, both in terms of poster design and presentational devices.

Allow the class to explore examples of scientific posters. Some examples with a space theme can be found on the Mars NASA website — see Useful Links.

STFC has a very relevant example of an informational poster on 'big telescopes' — see Useful Links. Please note and point out to student that this poster includes an outdated launch date for the James Webb Space Telescope.

It may be useful to look at other topic areas which can be found on the Activity web page — see Useful Links.

Identifying Features

Show students examples which demonstrate the standard of poster you expect from them.

Identify those features which students will include in their own posters.

This will vary depending on the age and ability of the class but may include the following:

- title
- subtitles
- paragraphs around themes
- graphs
- tables
- photographs
- captions
- bold/italic text
- definitions
- a careful balance between images and text

Research

Following this familiarisation with the writing genre, students will be ready to carry out research into their chosen area of focus. This could be related specifically to something they've learnt during their Deep Space Diary work, or another aspect of the Universe that they are interested in. Encourage them to use note-taking, book and e-research to compile information.

Planning/Design

Students should use the information they have gathered to draft a plan for their poster. They can be encouraged to evaluate and edit their plans. This is a nice opportunity for teacher, self or peer-led formative assessment.

Got notes? Write them here!

Writing

Allow several sessions for the poster creation. Students could produce their poster on large sheets of card or could use desktop publishing software if appropriate.

Presentation/Assessment

Depending on age/ability it may be appropriate for the class to present their posters to their peer group or another class. Encourage constructive peer feedback in line with current practices in your school.

Questions for the Class

- Where have you seen posters before? What have they been used for? What is their purpose?

- What are the main features of the scientific posters you have looked at?

- What makes scientific posters different/similar to other posters you have seen?

Additional Challenges / Extension Activities

Have more-able students complete a related scientific experiment and present their findings in poster form.

Students could build models and/ or present their work in a semi-permanent display for parents/other students to visit.

Ideas for Differentiation

Support:

- You may decide to use different strategies depending on the needs of the class. Consider voice-recordings as a way to engage reluctant writers at the planning stage.

- Consider the assistive technology available at your school to support dyslexic students. Typically, these students have lots of fantastic ideas, knowledge and understanding but may struggle with reading extended pieces of text or with organising their thoughts and ideas so they may be understood by others.

Challenge:

- Digital tools such as the Pic Collage app or MS Publisher could be used to extend more able students and enhance ICT skills.

Teacher Tip!

Collaging is a great way to support students who are less confident in art and design. Other students may enjoy sourcing images online, or even completing this activity on a computer.

CHAPTER FIVE
WORD SEARCH

Zap for the answers!

Find the words you've learnt in this chapter and add them to your Visual Dictionary of Deep Space at the back of the book.
Words can go forward, backward and diagonally.

P	P	B	I	R	P	L	R	G	C
L	B	M	N	A	W	A	E	A	I
A	D	V	F	T	D	I	M	L	R
N	F	J	O	S	I	T	O	A	E
E	H	Y	G	O	A	S	N	X	H
T	U	O	R	T	G	E	O	Y	P
G	M	X	A	O	F	L	R	S	S
O	P	D	P	R	U	E	T	H	O
Y	I	E	H	P	R	C	S	L	M
H	C	U	I	Y	K	C	A	T	T
Y	R	O	C	X	J	Z	D	B	A

Target = 8 words beginning with:

A D P A G P C I

Chapter Five: Word Search

CHAPTER FIVE WORD SEARCH

Find the words you've learnt in this chapter and add them to your Visual Dictionary of Deep Space at the back of the book. Words can go forward, backward and diagonally.

Target = 8 words beginning with:

A D P A G P C I

Background to this Activity

Word searches are a fun way to build your students' vocabularies. You can extend these activities with the Visual Dictionary of Deep Space (see below).

Running the Activity

The word searches provide an opportunity to review and discuss what has been covered in each chapter. For each word search, look at the starting letters noted below the word search grid. As a class or in student pairs, discuss what some of the words might be. Ask students if they can identify any of those words.

As students complete the word searches, remind them to write new words in their Visual Dictionary of Deep Space (see Activity 6.2).

Solutions to this Activity

CHAPTER FIVE WORD SEARCH

Zap for the answers!

Find the words you've learnt in this chapter and add them to your Visual Dictionary of Deep Space at the back of the book. Words can go forward, backward and diagonally.

P	P	B	I	R	P	L	R	G	C
L	B	M	N	A	W	A	E	A	I
A	D	V	F	T	D	I	M	L	R
N	F	J	O	S	I	T	O	A	E
E	H	Y	G	O	A	S	N	X	H
T	U	O	R	T	G	E	O	Y	P
G	M	X	A	O	F	L	R	S	S
O	P	D	P	R	U	E	T	H	O
Y	I	E	H	P	R	C	S	L	M
H	C	U	I	Y	K	C	A	T	T
Y	R	O	C	X	J	Z	D	B	A

Target = 8 words beginning with:

A D P A G P C I

Word Search Chapter 5: Astronomer, Data, Protostar, Atmospheric, Galaxy, Planet, Celestial, Infographic

Definitions:

Astronomer: an expert in astronomy

Data: facts and statistics collected together for reference or analysis

Resources Required

- Rulers
- Computers, devices or textbooks for research
- Pens/Pencils
- Visual Dictionary of Deep Space
- Tablet or device to access Zap code (optional — see Useful Links)

Useful Links

Visit **discoverydiaries.org/ activities/chapter-five-word-search** to download Zappar app content to use offline (PowerPoints, videos and image bundles etc.) and to access links to other info, which may be useful in planning and running this lesson.

Protostar: a baby star – a contracting mass of gas which represents the early stage of a star's formation

Atmospheric: relating to the atmosphere of Earth (or another planet)

Galaxy: a collection of gas, dust and millions or billions of stars, held together by mutual gravity

Planet: a spherical, celestial body moving in an elliptical orbit around a star

Celestial: positioned in or relating to the sky, or outer space, as observed in astronomy

Infographic: a visual representation of information or data e.g. as a chart or a diagram

Ideas for Differentiation

Support:

- Work as a class or in groups to find definitions, assigning words to students.

- Work as a class or in groups to create a song using vocabulary from the chapter.

- Provide hidden words to students.

Challenge:

- Once students have completed the word searches, ask them to develop their own. Download and print our blank word search template to use with your class (see Useful Links). They can then test a classmate with their word search. Differentiate by giving clues as the whole word, the first letter or a definition of the word.

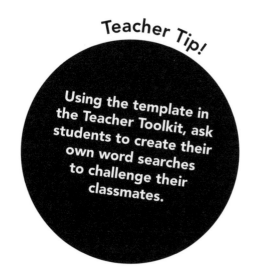

Teacher Tip!

Using the template in the Teacher Toolkit, ask students to create their own word searches to challenge their classmates.

Got notes? Write them here!

For ages 7–11

EXPLORE THE RED PLANET WITH THE MARS DIARY!

"The children loved it. The interactive element made them engaged from the start! Time effective, excellent lower ability differentiation [and] flexible enough that it allowed the children to progress through it at their own speed."

This popular sequel to the Principia Space Diary allows students to use their own creativity to place a mission to Mars where they explore the Martian surface and build a Mars habitat. Students use arts-based, visual learning to explore a wide range of STEM subjects while also learning what it takes to be a great scientist.

www.discoverydiaries.org/mars-diary

CHAPTER 6:
SPACE NEWS

Through their mission with the James Webb Space Telescope, students will have learnt some amazing facts about engineering, science, astronomy and the Universe we live in. In the final chapter of the programme, they will consolidate their learning through literacy and visual literacy activities.

What's inside this chapter?

6.1 – Deep Space Daily
Using research and information from other diary activities, write and illustrate a series of newspaper articles.
> Science + Literacy

6.2 – Visual Dictionary of Deep Space
Using words and images, add solutions from Word Search activities to the dictionary, then find their definitions.
> Science + Literacy

Activity 6.1: Deep Space Daily

Background to this Activity

The James Webb Space Telescope is our most advanced space telescope to date, helping us understand the Universe we live in. Scientists from across the world use Webb to study objects in space, so that we can learn more about our home planet and the history of our Universe.

But without the help and skills of science writers – sometimes called scientific journalists – the important findings of Webb can't be presented to the broader community, including other scientists, researchers and the general public. Since we can't all be space experts, we rely on scientific writers to provide a link between Webb's discoveries and the community. Communication plays an important role in helping us fully benefit from the important information Webb is collecting.

Literacy and visual literacy are excellent ways to engage students who may not be confident in STEM. This activity asks students to combine science and the arts by creating a four-page publication of space news.

Running the Activity

Prior Learning

This task should be the final stages of a short series of writing lessons focusing on the genre of report writing. Students should have opportunities to study a number of newspaper reports in class, prior to writing their own report. Here is a suggested plan for preceding lessons:

Lesson 1:

Look at a selection of newspaper articles and identify features which can be found in several of the examples (headlines, paragraphs, facts, speech, photos, etc). Make a list of these.

Lesson 2:

Look at some examples of catchy headlines in local newspapers. Focusing on headlines, encourage students to think of short and snappy headlines for a range of scenarios (cat stuck in tree, flooding,

Resources Required

- Selection of newspaper articles
- Books and internet access for research purposes

Useful Links

Visit **discoverydiaries.org/ activities/deep-space-daily** to access links to other info, which may be useful in planning and running this lesson.

celebrity visiting town, etc). They could work in groups to develop puns/catchy headlines to match the different scenarios.

Lesson 3:

Have students look at the five 'Ws' (who, what, when, where, why) and try to identify them in the different newspaper report examples (typically the introductory paragraph includes this information).

Deep Space Daily Task

Success Criteria

Pupils should be familiar with the features of newspaper article writing and should work with their teacher/educator to devise success criteria for their writing. Suggested success criteria include:

- headlines
- facts (not opinions)
- quotations
- photos and captions
- paragraphs
- connectives

Newspapers use headlines to grab your attention. Headlines try to tell the story in as few words as possible. Headlines may use alliteration/catchy slogans/puns.

Quotations tell us what has been said and who said it. They can help to tell the story by giving the reader the opinions of the people involved.

Photos help to tell the story by giving readers a snapshot of what happened, where it happened or who it happened to. Photos also need a caption underneath them. A caption is a short sentence explaining what is happening in the photograph.

Paragraphs help the reader clearly understand the information in the story. Each new paragraph could also be given a subheading. This is a very short title that tells the reader a little about what the paragraph will be about.

Research

Students' newspaper articles will obviously be based around discoveries in space. Depending on your class, you may decide to leave this task more open-ended or you may prefer to narrow students' choices to a few particular discoveries. Either way, before beginning to plan their article, students will need to carry out research using books and the internet to find out relevant facts to include in their article. Allow students to print out and collate notes for their newspaper reports.

Planning

Students will need time to plan their newspaper articles before they begin to write. A template has been included (see Useful Links), but you

Got notes? Write them here!

may wish to modify this or create your own, depending on the needs within your classroom.

Following this planning time, it may be a good idea to set aside some time for students to write the 'speech' parts of their articles, following separate success criteria for writing direct speech, for example.

Independent Writing

Students will use their plans to begin writing their newspaper articles. Remind them to keep an eye on the success criteria which you agreed on together as a class. Students could draw their own pictures, use pictures from the internet or create digital images using drawing software or apps.

Encourage students to use a dictionary and thesaurus throughout this task to improve the quality of their writing. You may also decide to provide a range of connectives in a word bank.

Self-Assessment

Students should check and edit their work as per the usual practice.

Have students revisit the success criteria when they are finished and make improvements where necessary. To inform Assessment-for-learning, you may want students to make a note of changes they have made at this point.

Peer-Assessment

With a copy of the success criteria in front of them, ask students to read and evaluate a peer's writing. Share examples between students of similar ability and use positive feedback techniques (e.g. two stars and a wish or similar).

Questions for the Class

- What are the main features we can find in newspaper articles?

- Who is the audience you are writing for?

- What are connectives? Can you identify any in your articles?

- What are the five 'Ws' (who/what/where/when/why) within your report?

Additional Challenges / Extension Activities

Working together, the class could compile a newspaper by drawing pieces from all class members, and produce copies of it to distribute to other classes in the school.

Ideas for Differentiation

Support:

- Group work/shared writing with the teacher/educator or paired work

- Provide students with word banks for challenging vocabulary

- Give students a particular 'discovery' to write about

_____

_____

_____

_____

_____

_____

_____

- Voice recorders could be used during the planning session to help students develop their ideas
- Pupils with Specific Learning Difficulties could use dictation software

Challenge:

- Students to type up and present their newspaper report using MS Publisher
- Students to read their report to another class
- Students to include a relevant web-link in the article
- Students to record sources in a bibliography to be handed in with the article

Teacher Tip!

The Teacher Toolkit includes an article planner, which will support students in structuring each of their articles. Allow students to experiment with different methods of communication, including visual literacy.

VISUAL DICTIONARY OF DEEP SPACE

What new words have you discovered in this book?
Create a visual dictionary of your new vocabulary so
that others can understand your technical lingo!

Word	Visual	Written Definition	Word	Visual	Written Definition
Webb		Short for the James Webb Space Telescope which is the biggest space telescope ever made. It folds out to the size of a tennis court!			

VISUAL DICTIONARY OF DEEP SPACE

Word	Visual	Written Definition	Word	Visual	Written Definition

Activity 6.2: Visual Dictionary of Deep Space

Background to this Activity

As students complete each of the four word searches in the Deep Space Diary, ask them to add the words they find to their dictionary. They can then research the definitions of those words and write them in the corresponding space and draw a picture.

Running the Activity

Start by building a word bank using the words found in the word searches. Students can contribute other scientific words they might have come across in completing other activities in their diary, which could be noted on cardboard or a whiteboard. Students can then use dictionaries to find the definitions of words, building their scientific vocabularies.

Once students have located the definitions of words, discuss as a class why we sometimes represent the meaning of words with symbols or images. Can students contribute examples of visual representations of words? Are there any examples in the classroom (e.g. an exit sign, a recycling guide, a sign indicating the location of a First Aid Kit)? What about other areas of the school (e.g. the signs on bathroom doors)? Note these down on a whiteboard to help support learning.

In small groups or pairs, students can then discuss how the meanings of the word search solutions might be represented visually. More capable students can use peer assessment to test how well a word has been represented visually.

Solutions from Word Searches

Word Search Chapter 2: Absorb, Light, Reflect, Gradient, Optical, Spectrum, Infrared, Prism

Word Search Chapter 3: Discovery, Construct, Experiment, Structure, Mirror, Method, Engineer, Payload

Word Search Chapter 4: Commands, Deploy, Program, Calibrate, Encryption, Sequence, Decode, Instrument

Resources Required

- Dictionaries – online and print
- Drawing materials

Useful Links

Visit **discoverydiaries.org/ activities/visual-dictionary-of- deep-space** to access links to other info, which may be useful in planning and running this lesson.

Word Search Chapter 5: Astronomer, Data, Protostar, Atmospheric, Galaxy, Planet, Celestial, Infographic

For additional words and definitions, see the Deep Space Glossary (see Useful Links).

Questions for the Class

- Why is it important to have definitions for words?

- What other scientific words do you know?

- What are some examples of when we represent words with symbols or images?

- Why do we sometimes represent words with images?

Additional Challenges / Extension Activities

Ask students to create acrostic poems, using the words in their Visual Dictionary.

Ask students to rearrange the letters of words from their dictionary, then test a partner to see if they can unjumble the words.

Ideas for Differentiation

Support:

- Work as a class or in groups to find definitions, assigning words to students.

- Work as a class or in groups to generate ideas around images that could be used to visually represent words.

- Students who are not confident drawers could cut pictures from magazines or source them from the internet to use as their visual representation.

Challenge:

- Ask students to use printed dictionaries, rather than searching online for definitions.

- In small groups, more capable students can review images, analysing their effectiveness and drawing conclusions as to why or why not.

Teacher Tip!

Encourage students to add to their dictionaries at the end of each chapter, so that they build their scientific vocabulary over the course of the programme.

Got notes? Write them here!

More titles in the Discovery Diaries series

Principia Mission Space Diary

Calling all Space Apprentices – ESA Astronaut Tim Peake needs your help!

Perfect for upper KS1/lower KS2 (or equivalent) students, the Space Diary follows Tim's mission to the International Space Station, from astronaut training to conducting experiments and observing Earth from space. With over 60 hours of curriculum-linked STEM-literacy activities, the Space Diary is fully supported with teaching notes for each activity, curriculum guides for England, Northern Ireland, Scotland and Wales, ideas for differentiation, extension activities and more. The diary's additional digital content enhances the learning experience, while students read, write, draw, experiment, code and decode their way through their mission. Access the Principia Mission Space Diary for free by signing up at **www.discoverydiaries.org**

Mission Mars Diary

Get ready for your mission to the red planet!

Take your KS2 (or equivalent) students on an adventure to Mars to search for signs of life. Using the Mars Diary, students plan and execute a mission with the help of their robot friends. Its 60+ hours of curriculum-linked STEAM activities build Science Capital while challenging students to recruit a crew, invent a rover, decode and analyse data and design a Martian habitat. This popular sequel to the Space Diary was written by Lucy Hawking and developed with the support of the UK Space Agency. Teaching notes, schedules, curriculum guides and ideas for differentiation made it easy to implement into any existing lesson plans. Access the Mission Mars Diary for free by signing up at **www.discoverydiaries.org**